Saving Home Energy

By Richard V. Nunn

Library of Congress Catalog Card Number: 75-2871

Manufactured in the United States of America

First Printing 1975

Saving Home Energy

Editor: Karen Phillips
Cover Photograph: Taylor Lewis

Contents

Introduction

You may ask how this nation got into the energy crunch. Authoritative answers will include politics, profit motive, waste, poor national planning, and energy depletion. All of these explanations are somewhat correct, but to be right about any of these issues will not solve the energy crisis or even help to solve it.

The real key to saving energy is to conserve and to use the available energy in a more practical way. That is what this book, *Saving Home Energy*, is all about. Some examples of ways to conserve energy follow:

1. If every American homeowner and apartment dweller kept the thermostat set at 68° for heat in the winter and at 78° for air conditioning in the summer, the nation could conserve about 550,000 barrels of oil daily.

2. If these same citizens would replace their present light bulbs with lower wattage bulbs, the nation would save about 100,000 barrels of oil daily.

Trying to divide and multiply the population of the United States in relation to the barrels of oil used per day is rather confusing. Moreover, this computation leads to questions of how one individual family, for instance yours, can conserve energy when conservation seems to boil down to a savings of only nickles and dimes.

Let's think about a few energy-saving steps that you could take:

1. If you have a ½-inch crack under your attic door, the heat loss can cost about $8 annually. To put weather stripping across this crack under the door will cost about $3. The first year you will only save $5, but in the next 10 years (or for the life of the weather stripping) you will save $80 to $100.

2. If you add 6 inches of ceiling insulation to your attic, the cost for an average house will be about $100. But annual monetary savings on heating will be $127. It will take just one year's savings on heating costs to pay for the insulation, and you will make a small profit. Multiply this investment over the 20-, 30-, or 40-year period that you may own the house, and you have a big monetary savings. What about energy savings? You will save about 63,757,469 BTUs (heat measurement) of heat this year and each successive year.

3. If you caulk and weather strip the windows and doors in your home, the cost for an average house will run about $20. The monetary savings on heat will be about $33 the first year; for the next 10 years, you will save $33 each year or about $330. You also save energy (BTUs).

So conserving energy saves money as well as the energy supply. We are not interested in who is to blame for the energy shortage, but only in how you can save money by saving energy in your home.

Bundle Your Home in a Blanket of Insulation

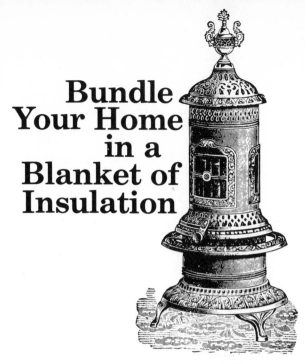

Insulating the floors, ceilings, and sidewalls will probably be the biggest home energy money saver. Insulation is fairly inexpensive, and it is easy to install yourself, which adds to the savings.

Figures compiled by the insulation industry show that a recommended 6 inches of loose fill insulation may be added to a home for about $107; this improvement will save about $127 annually in fuel charges. And, by cutting down on the home's heat loss, 64,451,755 BTUs of energy will be conserved annually. Or, if a 6-inch layer of batt insulation is added to a home, the cost will run about $100. You will save about $127 in heating costs, plus 63,757,469 BTUs of heat energy per year. These figures are based on a 2-story home with about 1500 square feet of living area.

Types of insulation available

Four basic types of insulation are available at most building material outlets and home center stores:

1. Rigid boards: insulation board sheathing and styrofoam boards.

2. Loose fill: Mineral wool, fiber glass wool, and vermiculite.

3. Blankets and batts: usually fiber glass.

4. Reflective: foil-backed gypsum board or thin paperlike sheets of foil.

Blanket and batt insulation often have a reflective surface on one side of the blanket or batt; the foil surface reflects heat and occasionally serves as a moisture barrier. Other moisture barriers that may be used with insulation include plastic or polyethylene film and an asphalt-impregnated paper covering.

Insulation board sheathing is used generally in new construction and remodeling; this product, since it is rigid and panelized, can't be installed like loose fill, bat, and blanket insulation.

We do not recommend any specific brand or type of insulation to buy; be guided by whatever material is easiest for you to install and, of course, by whatever you wish to pay.

Heat resistant factors

Whether you insulate your home yourself or have a professional do it, there are two insulation terms you should know: R values and U values.

An R value is a special measurement of insulation which represents the difficulty that heat has flowing through an insulation material. Insulation is rated in R values—the higher the R value, the greater the insulating value of the material. Most insulation has the R value stamped on it. Some typical values are R-21 for 7-inch thick blankets; R-21 for foil-faced insulation batts 7-inches thick; R-11 for 4-inch batts with a foil face; and R-11 for 3½-inch thick batts. The values vary according to thickness and quality of the product.

A U value indicates the insulation characteristics and/or heat transference of materials. U values are determined for all of the materials involved in the construction of a sidewall and not just the insulation. For example, the U value of a sidewall of a house would include the siding, sheathing, insulation, wallboard or plaster, and the air space in the wall. A low U value means good structural insulation.

Insulation alone may not lower the U value; you may need to use materials such as sheathing and siding to lower it.

How much insulation and where to put it

As a general rule, insulation may be added to existing walls, floors, and ceilings that are accessible. You can't add insulation to a wall that is finished with gypsum wallboard or plaster unless you remove the finished wall. However, loose fill insulation can be blown between the studs, siding, and finished wall, usually from the exterior, by a professional insulation contractor. This is not a do-it-yourself project; it takes special equipment to do an efficient job.

If you do have accessible construction, we recommend these insulation values:

For walls, use R-11 value insulation. If you choose fiber glass insulation, it will be 3½ inches thick.

For ceilings, use R-19 value. The thickness for fiber glass insulation with this R value is 6 inches.

For floors that are over unheated crawl spaces, we recommend insulation with an R-11 value, a 3½-inch thickness of fiber glass.

For crawl space walls, use R-11 value insulation; place the foil or moisture barrier on the inside of the crawl space.

For heated and partly heated basements, walls separating heated rooms from unheated rooms should be insulated with R-7 value material.

Insulation in new construction

If you're building a new house or an addition onto your existing home, insulation is easy and inexpensive to install. But there are many factors to consider such as design, construction, and methods. Here is a list of recommendations from the Electric Energy Association:

- Use double glazed windows to reduce heat transmission by approximately 50%.
- Close and seal passages and openings between unfinished attics and heated/cooled rooms. For example, seal the crack under an attic door.
- Make sure the damper (plate to control the draft) fits tightly, if you are adding a fireplace.
- Roof the house or an addition with light colored shingles to reflect the sun.
- Consider multilevel architectural designs. Multilevel designs usually incorporate smaller roof areas for a given amount of living space. For example, a 2-story house will have 15% less heat loss than will a ranch style house.
- Use 1 inch or more perimeter (curves around slabs) insulation for on-grade (on the ground) concrete slabs and footings.
- Have adequate attic ventilation to lessen the solar heat gains.
- Consider fewer and/or smaller windows; as much as 40% of all heating and cooling waste occurs here.
- Install thermal windows.
- Use solid core doors at exterior openings.
- Caulk cracks around door and window trim.
- Storm windows and doors cut heat loss by 30 to 50%.
- Leave all the trees around your house to eliminate summer heat gains.
- Insulate crawl spaces.
- Locate the water heater as close to the point of use as possible. For example, with a pipe run of 20 feet, you draw 2 quarts of cool water before the hot water reaches the faucet. Annually, this amounts to 1,000 or more gallons of water that you pay to heat but are unable to use.
- Install a thermostat which will automatically lower the room temperature during sleeping hours.
- Install fluorescent fixtures where you can; they burn less electricity than incandescent fixtures.
- Insulate pipes and ducts to prevent heating and cooling waste.

Insulation products

General insulation products vary slightly according to the manufacturer. Products and descriptions include:

Reverse flange batts. These may have a foil or kraft paper vapor barrier on one side; the other side has a breather kraft paper barrier. The material is used primarily for insulating crawl spaces.

Foil-faced fiber glass insulation. The material is made in rolls and batts and is faced with an aluminum foil vapor barrier. The insulation is made for general application.

Paper-faced fiber glass insulation. The fiber glass rolls and batts have a black kraft paper vapor barrier. Use this product for general application.

Plain fiber glass rolls. Sold in rolls and batts, this insulation may be used with a vapor barrier such as 2-mil polyethylene film or gypsum wallboard with a foil back.

Sill sealer. This thin fiber glass insulation is used between a masonry foundation wall and a sill plate. The material compresses to about a 1/32-inch thickness.

Loose wool. This material is usually made of fiber glass, and it may be poured into open attic floors. Loose wool is sold in bags; one bag is adequate for covering about 25 square feet of space with a 4-inch thickness.

Blown wool insulation. This insulation must be installed by a professional; it is blown into sealed areas with a pneumatic blowing machine.

Vermiculite insulation. This is an expanded mica product that is sometimes mixed with pellets of styrofoam. It may be used the same way as loose wool insulation is used, or it may be blown into air spaces with special equipment.

Rigid insulation. This material is made of insulation board sheathing or styrofoam boards. The sheathing is used in new construction and remodeling; the styrofoam boards may be used as add-on insulation between studs, joists, and rafters, or the boards may be used as a duct insulation.

Know Your BTUs

A BTU is a measure of heat; the letters BTU stand for British Thermal Unit. BTUs are used frequently in regard to insulation products and systems. One BTU is the amount of heat needed to raise the temperature of 1 pound or 1 pint of water 1° F. To define BTU another way, 1 BTU is the amount of heat produced by 1 kitchen match.

Bthu is another heat term; it is a measurement of the number of BTUs that will flow through material in 1 hour. The output of heating and cooling equipment (furnaces and air conditioners) is usually expressed in Bthus.

A therm is used in the measurement of natural or coal gas; it is the amount of heat equal to 100,000 BTUs.

This home shows no visible loss or gain of heat.

The heat that has escaped from the same home is revealed in this infrared photograph. The heat loss is especially pronounced beneath the picture window where a heating unit is located. Heat has also escaped from the chimney (white spot on top of roof). Heat loss may be reduced with adequate insulation. This house was used in a test run by Owens-Corning Fiberglas Corporation.

Does your home have enough insulation? You may get an indication by checking the roof of your home after a snowfall. The first home (duplex) probably has adequate insulation since the snow on the roof is not melting; heat does not seem to be escaping through the roof. The second home probably doesn't have adequate insulation since the snow on the roof is rapidly melting due to heat lost through the roof. If you live in an area where snow is minimal, check the amount of insulation in the attic.

Fiber glass insulation looks like this. Thickness of fiber glass is rated by R values; a high R value means greater insulation. Fiber glass insulation is manufactured in blankets and batts. The material may have a foil or paper vapor barrier attached to one or both sides.

Foil vapor barriers look like this. The paper flanges (rims) along the edges are used for fastening the insulation to studs, joists, and rafters. You can buy single or multiple layers of foil for insulation; the type you should choose depends on the R value required to adequately insulate your home. Polyethylene film may also serve as a moisture barrier in sealing off crawl spaces.

Loose fill insulation is composed of expanded mica or a combination of expanded mica and styrofoam. This material is poured between floor joists or professionally blown between the studs of a house to insulate the sidewalls. R values depend on the thickness of the loose fill insulation. If you choose this product to insulate your home, ask your building material retailer to calculate your needs according to the R value that you want.

Mineral wool is a loose fill insulation that is used between floor joists or blown into sidewalls. Loose fill insulation is ideal for open attic floors and areas that are difficult to insulate with batt, blanket, or rigid insulation.

Styrofoam is a rigid insulation which is extremely lightweight and may be used to insulate between furring strips. Styrofoam is also a good product with which to insulate heating or cooling ducts.

Insulation board sheathing is rigid insulation that is generally used in new construction and remodeling. Insulation board sheathing is also rated according to R value; you may not need additional batt, blanket, or loose fill insulation when insulation board sheathing is used.

Sill (plate on foundation) sealer insulation is used between foundation walls and the sill in new construction and remodeling. Sill sealer is narrow and may be compressed tightly when sandwiched between the foundation wall and the sill.

How to install insulation

Staple insulation to the inside faces of studs, rafters, and joists. Space the staples about 5 inches apart. Make sure that the edges to be stapled along each side of the insulation fit tightly against the framing members (studs, rafters, and joists). The vapor barrier should face the warm side of the room. When insulating floors, the vapor barrier should face upward. When insulating walls, start stapling the insulation from the top and work down. Make sure the ends of the insulation fit tightly against the top and bottom plates (framing members).

Insulation must fit behind obstructions such as wall outlets and pipes. If you have to cut the insulation to fit, make sure the vapor barrier is not damaged. If you puncture the vapor barrier, patch it with a piece of scrap vapor barrier and contact adhesive.

To insulate around doors and windows where the full widths of insulation materials cannot be used, stuff small amounts of insulation into the spaces; then cover the insulation with scraps of vapor barrier.

Insulation should go behind floor bridging wherever possible. If you cannot fit the insulation behind the bridging, fit it against the bridging; then cover the gap with vapor barrier. The insulation must be as continuous as possible.

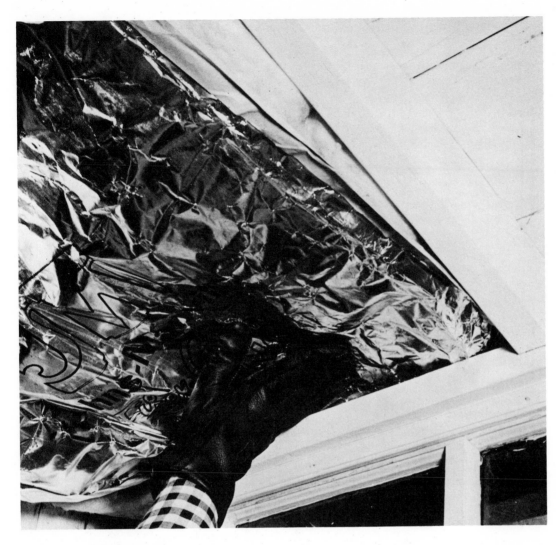

To insulate ceilings, fit insulation to the outside framing member. Form a stapling flange (edge) by peeling back the insulation from the vapor barrier. The insulation must fit tightly against the plate. Staple the edges of the insulation to the inside faces of the framing members every 5 inches. For reflective insulation, allow about 1 inch of air space between the ceiling and insulation. In attics, first insulate across the collar beams that tie the rafters together, then insulate between the wall studs. Do not use a continuous blanket; cut and fit the insulation to each element. Vapor barrier material may be used to cover the splices in the insulation. Leave ventilation space above collar beams (see drawing).

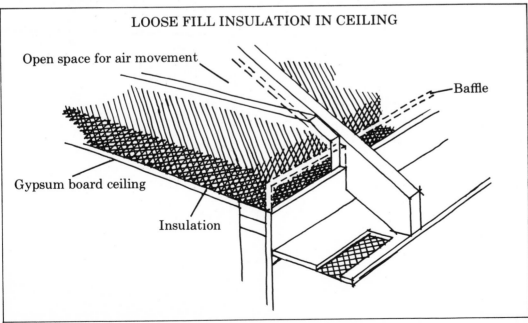

LOOSE FILL INSULATION IN CEILING

Open space for air movement

Baffle

Gypsum board ceiling

Insulation

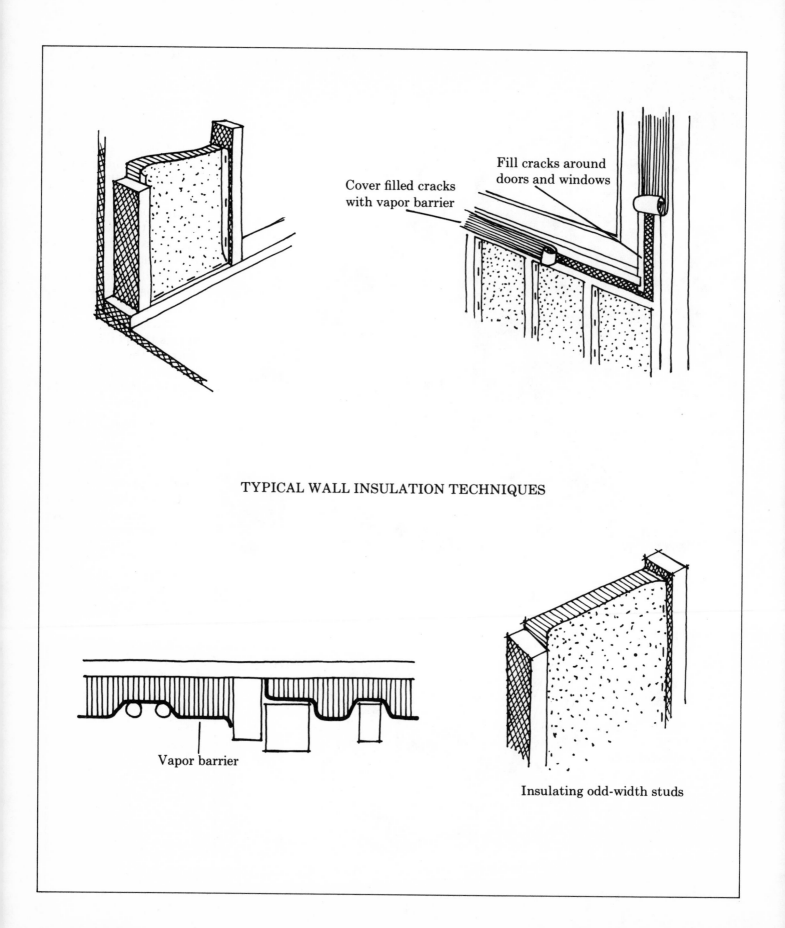

Cover filled cracks
with vapor barrier

Fill cracks around
doors and windows

TYPICAL WALL INSULATION TECHNIQUES

Vapor barrier

Insulating odd-width studs

HOW TO INSULATE CRAWL SPACES

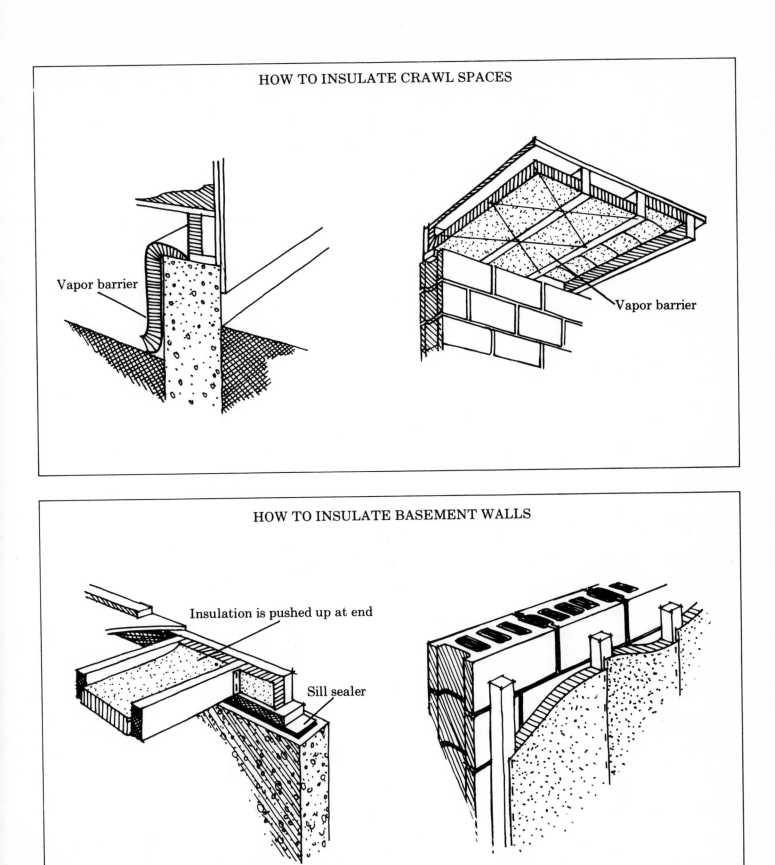

Vapor barrier

Vapor barrier

HOW TO INSULATE BASEMENT WALLS

Insulation is pushed up at end

Sill sealer

HOW TO INSULATE PERIMETERS

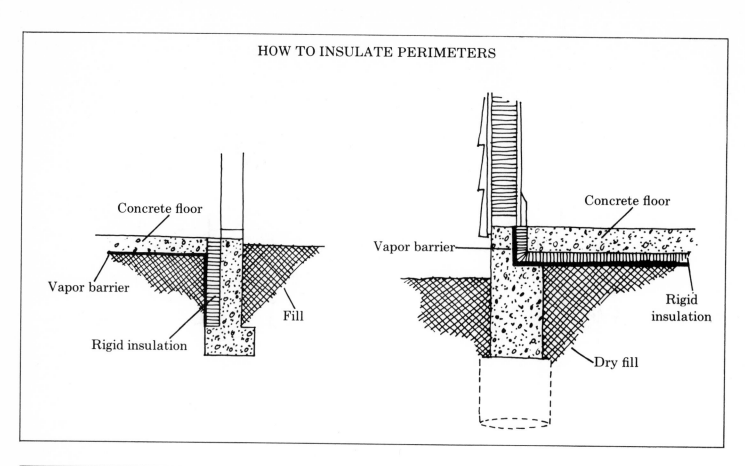

Concrete floor

Vapor barrier

Rigid insulation

Fill

Concrete floor

Vapor barrier

Rigid insulation

Dry fill

VENTILATION FOR CRAWL SPACES

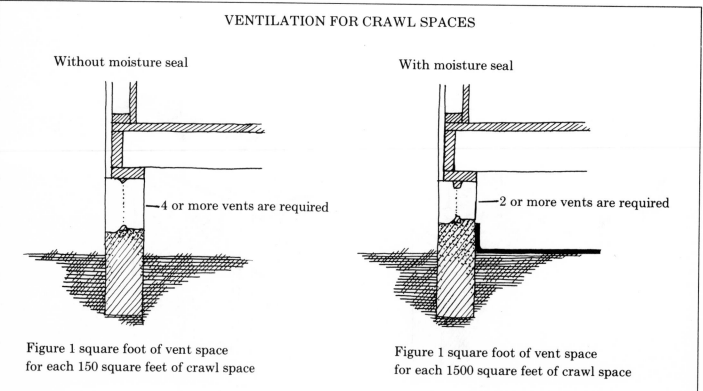

Without moisture seal

4 or more vents are required

Figure 1 square foot of vent space
for each 150 square feet of crawl space

With moisture seal

2 or more vents are required

Figure 1 square foot of vent space
for each 1500 square feet of crawl space

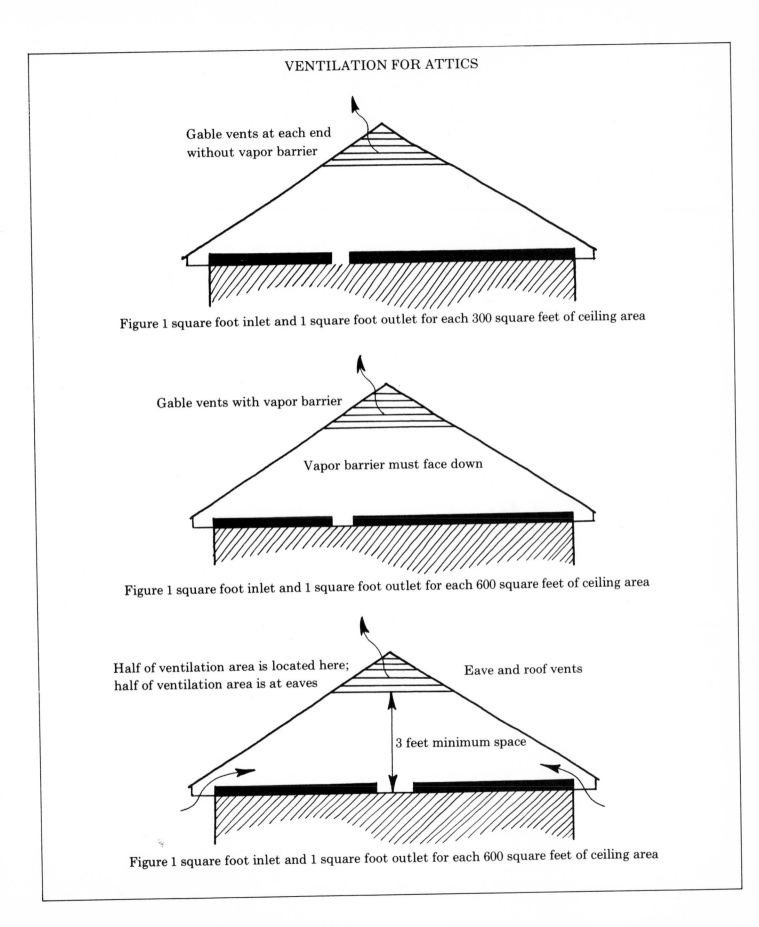

Gable vents at each end without vapor barrier

Figure 1 square foot inlet and 1 square foot outlet for each 300 square feet of ceiling area

Gable vents with vapor barrier

Vapor barrier must face down

Figure 1 square foot inlet and 1 square foot outlet for each 600 square feet of ceiling area

Half of ventilation area is located here; half of ventilation area is at eaves

Eave and roof vents

3 feet minimum space

Figure 1 square foot inlet and 1 square foot outlet for each 600 square feet of ceiling area

Rigid styrofoam insulation may be glued or tacked to wall surfaces. Since this material will probably be covered with a finished wall such as gypsum wallboard or paneling, the styrofoam can be sandwiched between the furring strips which will be used to fasten the paneling. Sheets of 2-mil polyethylene film or a reflective foil vapor barrier should be installed over the styrofoam and furring strips.

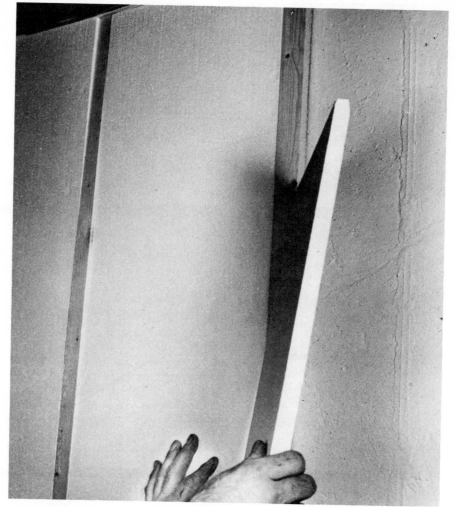

Working with Insulation

Installing fiber glass or loose fill insulation is not dangerous, but taking some precautionary measures will ensure your comfort.

1. Wear leather gloves when working with fiber glass. Tiny fibers tend to work themselves into the pores of your skin, and they can cause discomfort. Also, wear a shirt with long sleeves to protect your arms.

2. Wear safety glasses when working with insulation.

3. When working with loose fill insulation, ventilate the room, if possible; loose fill insulation may be dusty.

Degree Day Measurements

The term degree day may come up in conversations between insulation salesmen and builders. A degree day is a number, based on your local U.S. Weather Bureau data, that represents the severity of winter weather. Builders and manufacturers of building materials use these degree day numbers to estimate the heating requirements of your home.

The degree day number for winter days is computed by subtracting the day's mean temperature from 65° F. For example, if the third day in December was 50° F., the degree day would be 15.

Caulking and Weather Stripping

Those tiny cracks around windows, in the siding, in foundation walls, and under doors are all sources of heat loss. If you own an average-size house, you can save up to 17,000,000 BTUs of heat annually by filling the tiny cracks with caulking compound and weather stripping. The cost of caulking and weather stripping materials is approximately $20, and the heat savings the first year is about $33.

Also, consider these figures:

Envision 1000 houses like yours. If you and your 999 counterparts add about 6 inches of ceiling insulation to your homes and caulk and weather strip the doors, windows, and cracks, the energy saved in heating for 1 year would supply necessary energy to another 593 homes. Your cost will be about $150. Your savings will amount to approximately $200 the first year. After your initial investment is paid, you will save about $200 per year for an indefinite period.

Caulking: you have a big choice

The 5 basic types of caulking are:

1. Silicone. This caulking is expensive—usually more costly than other types. However, the material will withstand the elements for years. Silicone caulking may be used on most surfaces, but does not adhere well to paint.

2. Latex. This fast-drying material works well with paint. Latex caulking is water thinned; therefore, tools used in working with it are easy to clean.

3. Oil-base. This standard compound is inexpensive, and it will adhere to almost any surface.

4. Butyl rubber. This caulking will last for years. It is fairly expensive; use it mainly for caulking joints between metal and masonry surfaces such as placed concrete, concrete blocks, brick, and stone.

5. Polyvinyl acetate. This caulking is medium priced and may be used for any surface. It adheres well to painted surfaces.

You may buy caulking two ways: in cartridges and in bulk. We recommend cartridges; they are made to use with a caulking gun and are disposable. Cartridge caulking compound utilizes a half-barrel caulking gun. For about $1.50 you can buy a gun that may be used indefinitely.

Where to caulk

Cracks and splits that need to be caulked at your house may or may not be obvious. Below is a checklist that may be helpful:

- [ ] Between joints in siding
- [ ] Between window casings and siding
- [ ] Under windowsills
- [ ] Under thresholds of doors
- [ ] Between door casings and siding
- [ ] Between dissimilar materials (brick and wood)
- [ ] At the bottom of siding
- [ ] At moldings (drip caps) over windows and doors
- [ ] Joints in fixed storm windows
- [ ] Between foundations and siding
- [ ] Around exterior electrical outlets
- [ ] Around exterior dryer vents
- [ ] In partially split siding
- [ ] Tops and bottoms of porch columns
- [ ] Under eaves and gable moldings
- [ ] Around gable vents
- [ ] At electrical wire inlets
- [ ] Cracks between windowsills and trim or frames
- [ ] Cracks between thresholds and doorframes
- [ ] At dormer cheeks and roof shingles

Caulking clean up

Caulking is a sticky material; after each job you will have to clean up the caulking gun as well as caulking that has splattered.

- If the caulking is silicone, you may wipe off excess caulking with a clean cloth; do this immediately. If you are not able to clean up at once, use mineral spirits on a soft cloth to remove the excess.
- Butyl rubber caulking is solvent in mineral spirits.
- Polyvinyl acetate caulking comes off with xylene or toluene solvent.
- Use water to clean up latex caulking.
- Oil-based caulking wipes clean with mineral spirits or naphtha.

Types of weather stripping and where to buy them

There are literally dozens of weather stripping materials on the market. You will find selections at home centers, building material outlets, hardware stores, and variety stores; materials may also be found in general merchandise catalogs and some drugstores.

Prices vary from a few pennies to several dollars; weather stripping is not expensive and it is very easy to install. The only tools that you'll need are a hammer and a hacksaw or tinsnips.

The basic types of weather stripping are:

1. Strips that are surface mounted
2. Metal (usually aluminum or brass) and plastic combinations
3. Metal and fabric combinations
4. Plastic
5. Fabric
6. Brass strips
7. Aluminum strips

Weather stripping is classified as:
1. Window weather stripping
2. Door weather stripping
3. Combination window and door weather stripping
4. Garage door weather stripping

As a rule, the proper application is marked on weather stripping packages. You can also purchase weather stripping kits for windows and doors; these kits come with fastening devices such as nails and adhesive.

Installing weather stripping

Surface-mounted weather stripping and concealed weather stripping have their own type of fasteners, usually nails or glue. The secret to installing either type of material is to space the fasteners according to the manufacturer's instructions. You should also make sure that the weather stripping is not tangled when you apply it; the strips should be tightly fastened and smooth. If the strips are bent, especially the metal and combination metal and plastic types, it is almost impossible to straighten them. If you bend a strip and can't straighten it, throw the damaged strip away and work with a new one. Defective weather stripping is worthless.

How and where to use caulking

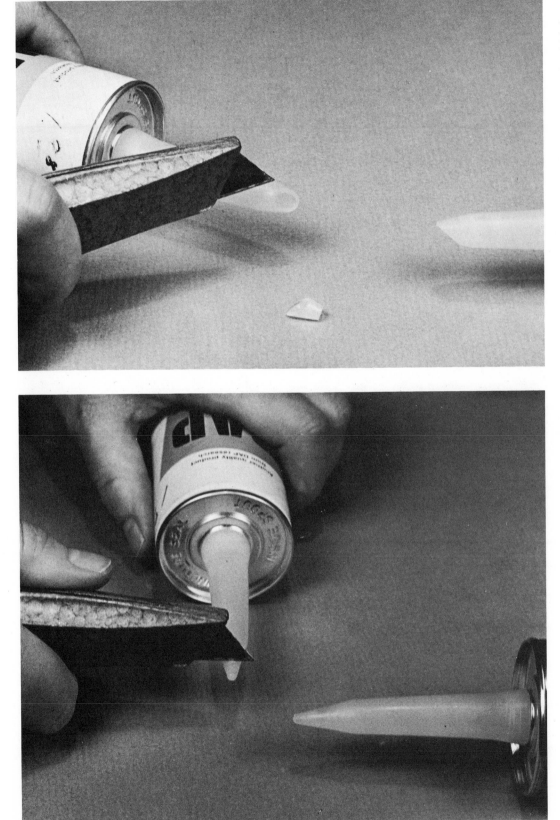

Caulking cartridge nozzles are made of a plastic material. The nozzle must be cut at a 45° angle so that the caulking may be properly applied. Cut the nozzle, which is tapered, with a sharp razor knife. The farther back from the end you cut the nozzle, the wider the caulking strip will be. Some nozzles are faintly marked with caulking widths such as ⅜ inch and 5⁄16 inch. You simply cut the nozzle at the line for the desired width.

To fill large holes with caulking, cut squarely across the nozzle. You don't need to cut on an angle since the caulking flows straight into the hole. At times, you may not be able to caulk the defect with the gun and cartridge combination. In this event, squirt some caulking onto the blade of a putty knife and use it to trowel the caulking into the hole.

Caulking cartridge guns have a notched plunger which pushes the caulking compound out of the nozzle. A great deal of pressure on the caulking material is generated by the plunger. At the end of each caulking run turn the plunger, as shown, to take pressure off the caulking cartridge. This stops the flow of caulking almost immediately.

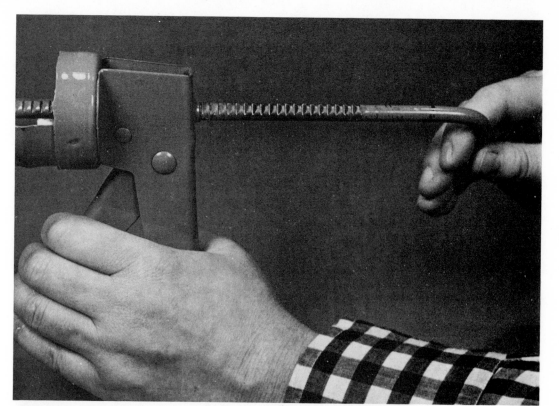

Remove old, cracked caulking with a putty knife or scraper before you apply new caulking; the joint or crack must be clean and free of loose debris. If the existing caulking is tight and in place, you do not have to remove it. To determine whether the old caulking is solid, probe with a putty knife.

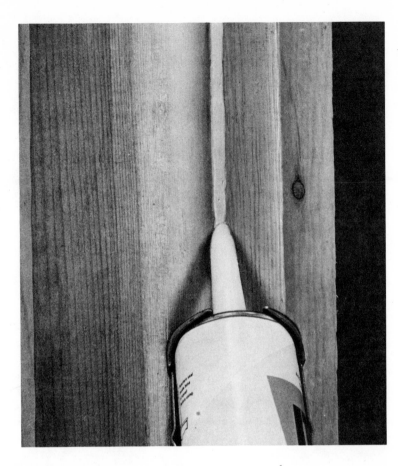

Straight, open cracks are easy to caulk by quickly moving the caulking gun down the crack. Hold the gun at about a 45° angle to the work; move it down the crack as you pull the trigger. You have to time the downward movement with the trigger pressure so that the caulking will flow smoothly into the crack.

Caulking lap or drop siding takes a special technique. Keep pressure on the trigger of the gun as you progress downward to fill the crack. When you get to the lap, push the nozzle of the caulking cartridge up under the lap siding. Fill the entire crack with one motion; do not start and stop the caulking process. You will have to move the gun downward fairly rapidly to prevent a buildup of caulking compound.

Caulking and Weather Stripping   23

If you find breaks in the caulking of cracks and joints, they are usually caused by moving the caulking gun too quickly along the crack or joint. The problem may also be caused by air bubbles in the cartridge or a faulty plunger. To get a smooth caulking line, pull the caulking gun downward, press the trigger, and control the flow of the cartridge by the speed of the downward movement.

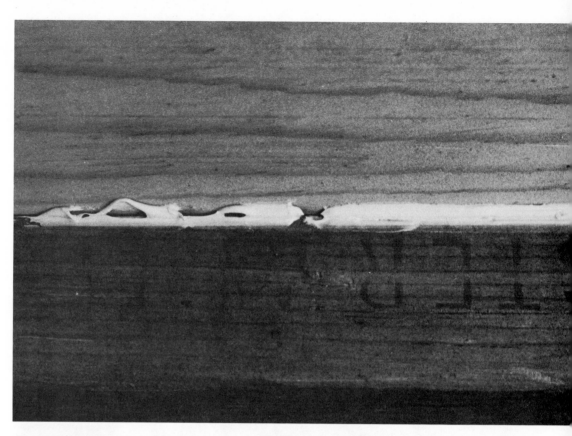

Ridges in the caulking compound are usually caused by moving the caulking gun too slowly down the crack or joint. The ridges are a build-up of caulking compound. Again, the trick is to move the gun at the same rate as the flow of the caulking compound. Ideally, the caulking compound should slightly bead (be raised) on the surfaces of both sides of the joint or crack.

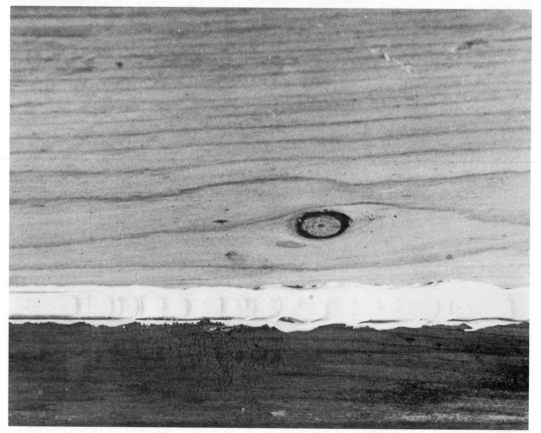

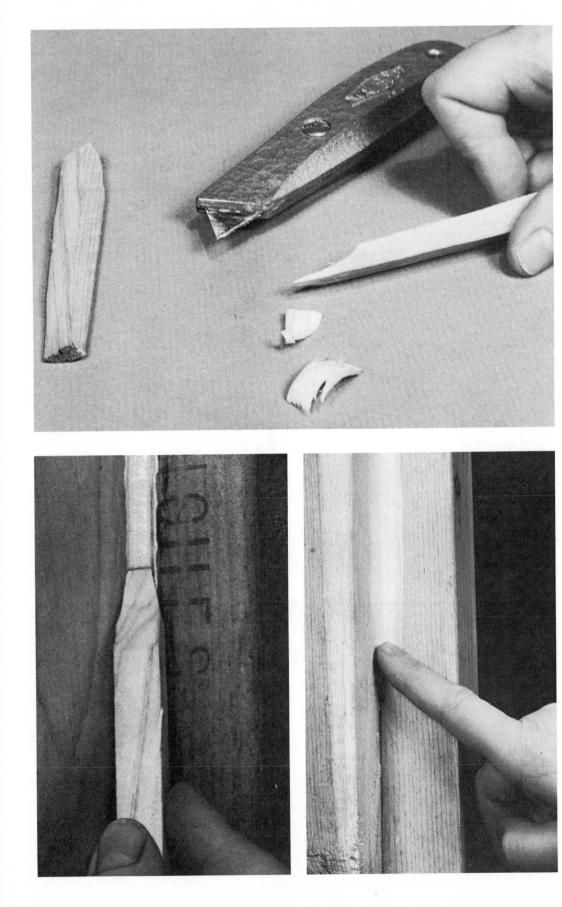

To smooth caulking that has ridges, carve a piece of wood into this configuration. Or, square off the end of an ice cream stick, tapering its edge like a chisel bevel. The width of the stick should be about 1/16″ wider than the width of the caulking line.

Far left:
Wet the smoothing stick with water. Then, run the beveled edge lightly down the caulking bead. Work slowly, and rewet the stick frequently. The water keeps the caulking compound from sticking to the wood. If the joint or crack is full of caulking compound, but untidy, don't try to remove the caulking. Smoothing the caulking is easier than removing it and starting again.

Left:
Smoothing ridges and skipped areas in latex caulking is easy to do with a wet finger since latex caulking is water-based. Caulking compounds come in 3 basic colors: white, black, and grey. Depending on the job, you should pick a color that matches or blends with the surrounding material. After the caulking dries and has a crust on its top surface, you may paint the surface.

Metal-to-masonry joints should be caulked with butyl rubber caulking. Although it is fairly expensive (about $2 per cartridge), butyl rubber caulking will last for many years and will withstand the expansion and contraction of metal and masonry. There are no special techniques involved in applying butyl caulking to joints and cracks.

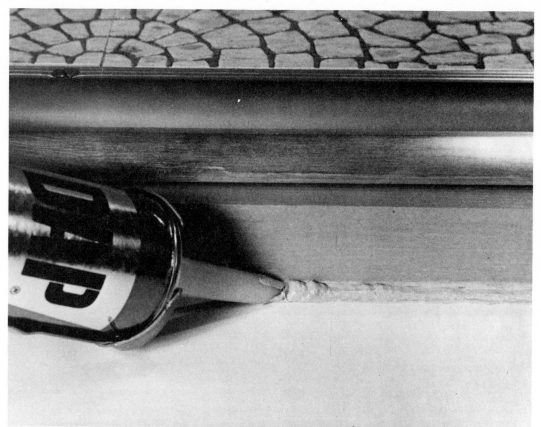

Keep unused caulking fresh by plugging the nozzle of the caulking cartridge with a screw or piece of dowel rod. The diameter of the plug should be just a bit smaller than the hole in the nozzle. If the plug is too large, it may damage the nozzle, thus preventing the caulking from flowing evenly into a crack or joint.

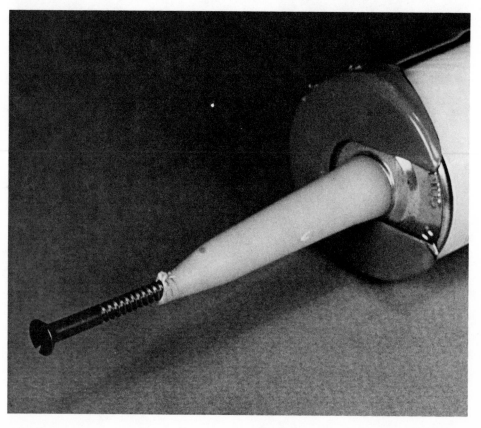

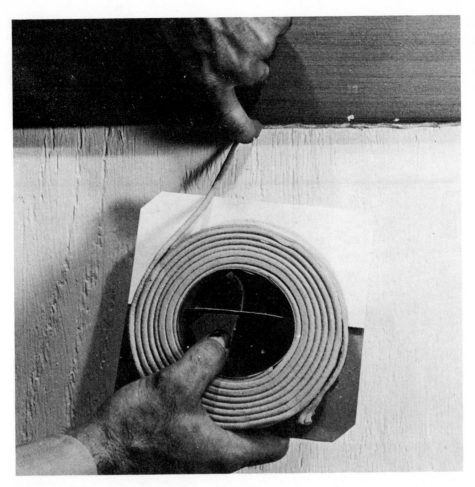

Rope or cord caulking may be purchased by the roll; it is more substantial than regular cartridge or bulk caulking. You simply unroll the caulking and press it into place with your fingers or a putty knife. Rope caulking may be used anywhere cartridge or bulk caulking is used. However, the caulking should be used in cracks and joints no wider than the diameter of a pencil.

Damaged siding can waste energy

Split and broken siding will eventually lead to heat loss or gain within your home. Also, damaged siding can cause water leaks which in turn will cause basic structural problems for your house. If the siding on your home is in poor condition, you should consider re-siding the house. If you decide to re-side the house, be sure to deal with a reputable contractor; he will be able to specify siding, such as aluminum, vinyl, or wood, that protects and insulates at the same time.

Small splits in siding can be repaired with caulking compound. If the wood is broken but still intact, coat the base of the break with caulking compound, as shown, and press the damaged wood back into position. The caulking compound has enough adhesion to hold the wood in place; it will also seal and waterproof the break. If the siding is painted, you may have to spot prime the patched area so that it matches the surrounding siding.

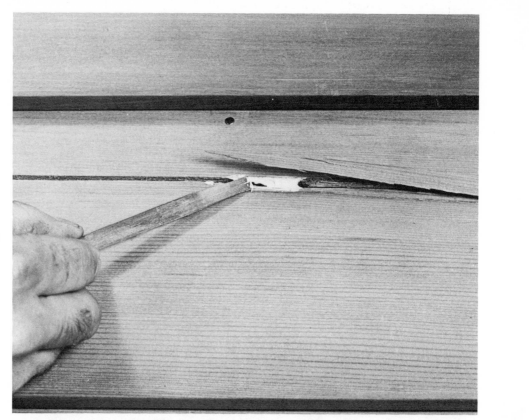

If the siding is just split and not broken, you can seal the break with caulking compound. Use plenty of pressure on the caulking gun to force the caulking material into and in back of the split. Since the split will probably be narrow, excess caulking compound will spill over onto the sid-ing. You can remove this excess with mineral spirits or naphtha— depending on the type of caulking that you use.

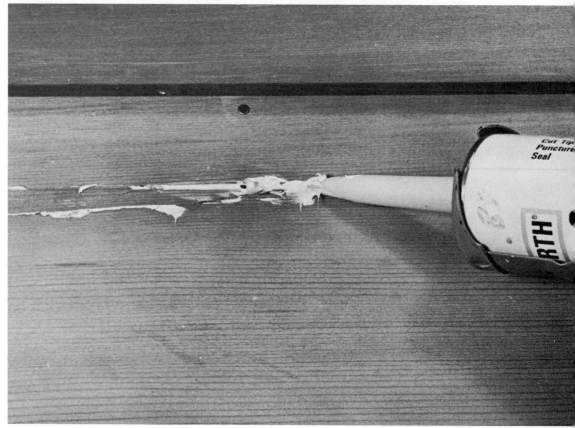

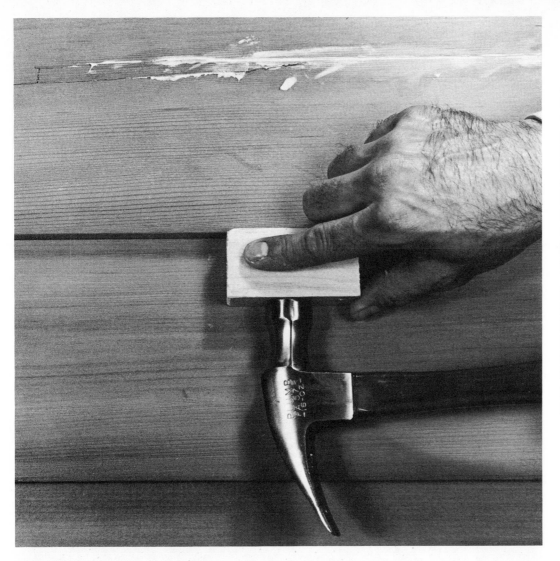

If you have wide splits in the siding, fill them with caulking compound. Then, tap the split together with a hammer. A piece of scrap wood serves as a buffer block between the siding and the face of the hammer, which prevents further damage to the siding. You may need a helper to tightly nail the split in the siding while you hold the split together. However, before nailing, make sure the split is full of caulking compound to obtain the proper sealing effect.

Use plenty of nails around the break in the siding. The split has to be tightly sealed with caulking compound and secured with nails; this will prevent it from pulling apart with expansion and contraction caused by high and low temperatures. Ringed nails, which have greater holding power, are recommended for this repair.

Replace damaged siding, if the damage is major. Square the damaged section, as shown. If the siding is made of aluminum or vinyl, you can remove the entire strip and replace it. You will have to go from joint to joint and will use the same techniques as shown here for wood siding. For asbestos shingles and cedar shakes, the same wedging techniques are used as for individual shingle units.

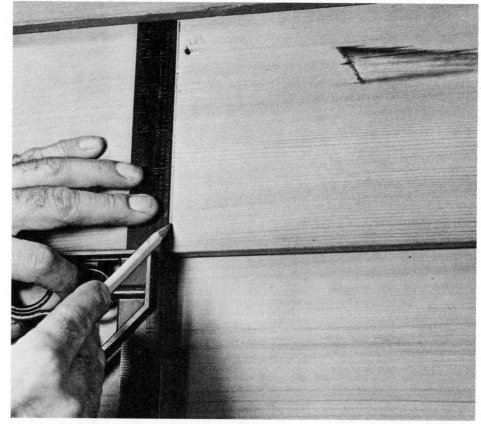

Drive wedges under the damaged siding to separate it from the sheathing below. The butt ends of cedar shingles make perfect wedges. You will need several wedges to properly elevate the siding for removal. When you drive the wedges home, be careful not to damage the siding below the broken area. A thin piece of cardboard may be used to eliminate hammer tracks on the course of siding below. Slip the cardboard under the joint of the siding.

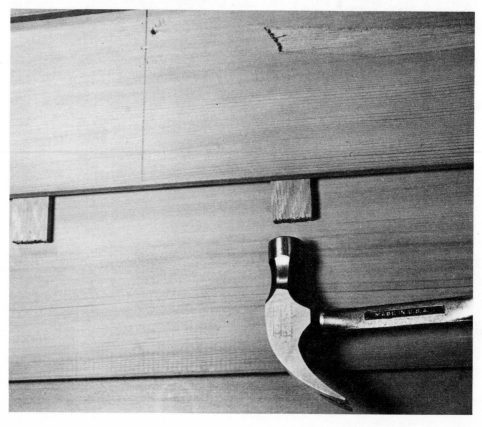

Cut the damaged siding, after it has been properly wedged, with a backsaw or a handsaw with a combination blade. This is a tedious process, since you cannot get a full stroke on the saw. Take it easy; cut slowly until you separate the good siding from the bad siding. Hand pressure on the back of the saw blade will help speed the cutting operation.

Insert the new siding under the above existing siding, which is spread open by the wedges. After the replacement piece is in position, check the alignment with the adjoining siding; a carpenter's level may be used to make sure the siding is square with the adjoining pieces. Sheathing is often covered with asphalt-impregnated building paper, which is usually black in color; it is used as a moisture or vapor barrier and it should be continuous for the best insulation value. If you damage the paper in the replacement process, patch it with new paper.

Caulking and Weather Stripping   31

Nail the new siding patch to the sheathing about every 4 inches. Use ringed nails at both the top and bottom of the siding patch and at the junction of the new siding and the old siding. To properly seal the new siding patch and the old siding patch, you may have to renail the old siding to close the joints. All siding, such as wood, aluminum, and vinyl, should be tightly nailed.

Seal the joints between the new siding and the old siding with caulking compound. The joints should be full; don't skimp. Patched siding tends to buckle along the bottom joint. Several months after you replace a section of siding, check to see if the bottom joint is open. If so, try renailing the joint shut. If there is still a gap, fill the opening with caulking compound.

Felt weather stripping, or a combination of metal and felt, is an old standby. This weather stripping is easy to install with nails or screws, and the material is very inexpensive. We do not recommend any one type of weather stripping. Most of the weather stripping bought at building material outlets and hardware stores is effective.

Pliable gasket weather stripping has self-adhesive; simply remove the adhesive backing and stick the weather stripping into place. Pliable gasket material may be used for both windows and doors. Thickness varies depending on the crack to be sealed. Metal strip weather stripping is made of brass, bronze, or aluminum, and it has a V-like crimp (fold) to block heat loss. To install the strips, start with the hinge side of the door, and nail the strip onto the jamb. Be careful not to crease the strip; it is very thin. The strip should be fastened to the doorframe so that it fits tightly against the stop. On the latch side of the door, install the top strip down to the strike plate. Then, fit the weather stripping around the strike, and nail on the bottom section. The top piece may have to be slightly mitered at the corners for side strip clearance.

Garage door weather stripping is pliable. The material is nailed to the bottom of a garage door to prevent drafts. This weather stripping may also be nailed to the top jamb of the garage door, if there is a gap. Space the nails about 3 or 4 inches apart. Weather stripping should fit smoothly; incorrect nailing may cause gaps. Start at one end and nail across the door; don't fasten the material at both ends and work toward the center.

Nail metal or plastic weather stripping at both ends, then work toward the center. Lightly tack the material into position, then go back and drive the nails home; be careful not to strike the metal too hard with the hammer. Hard blows will bend weather stripping and produce gaps. Gaps will cause the weather stripping to lose its insulation value.

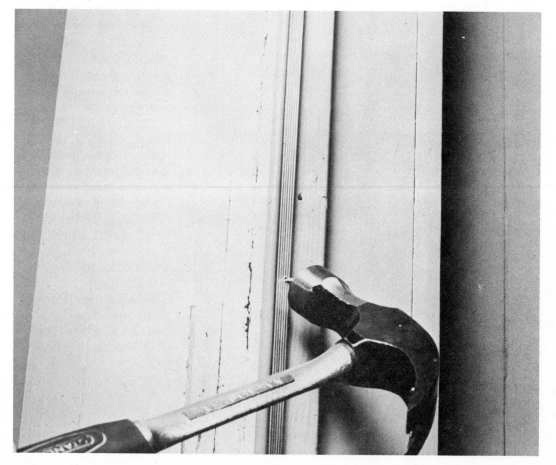

Seal the top of the door as well as the sides. To correctly position weather stripping, close the door and fit the weather stripping against it. After the weather stripping has been lightly tacked into position, open the door to make nailing easier. If the weather stripping has self-adhesive backing, close the door or window, and fit the material tightly against the door or window frame.

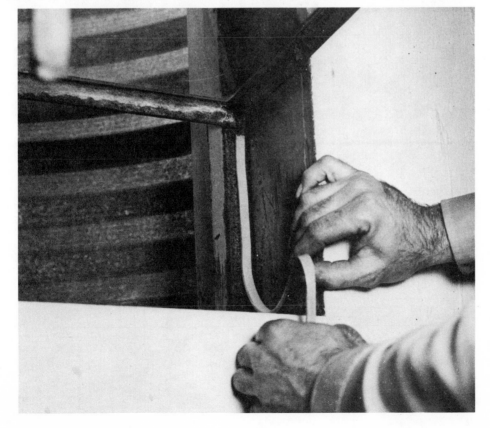

Basement windows, which are often made of metal, are famous for heat loss or gain since weather stripping for them is frequently overlooked. The self-adhesive pliable gasket weather stripping is ideal for basement windows; simply run the material around the metal frame of the window and close it. Also, plastic well covers for windows help to save energy; they are fastened to the metal window well inserts. Plastic covers are for year-round use; they are left permanently in position. The covers are fairly expensive—about $25 to $30 each.

Threshold sweep strips come in kit form for exterior doors and storm doors. There are several varieties available; some are plastic and some have a felt strip attached to a metal strip. The strips are easy to install with nails or screws; they should run the complete length of the door bottom. If you apply the sweep strips to the exterior door, be sure to allow (if necessary) for the thickness of the carpeting.

Transparent weather stripping tape may be used to insulate cracks around windows. Start the strip at the top of the window and work down. Pull off as much tape as you need for the job and cut it to this length. Then, carefully press the tape into position along the window trim and frame. The tape is extremely sticky; you may have to pull it up and reposition it to properly cover the crack.

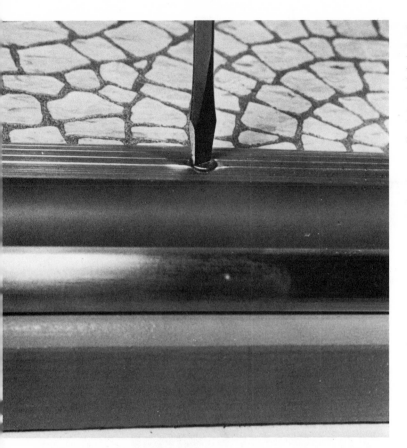

Gasket threshold strips are available in several types. A threshold gasket is shown with the threshold. The strip is attached to the floor at the threshold with screws. Another type is a vinyl bubble strip which is fastened to the bottom of the door. You may need a new metal threshold with the bubble strip. If so, you will have to remove the old threshold with a short pry bar. You may have to cut the threshold at the ends where it fits against the door jambs; if so, use a hacksaw. Then put in the new threshold; it should fit directly below the door when the door is closed.

Screw the new threshold into position; caulk the ends and the crack between the threshold and floor. The vinyl bubble strip needs ½-inch clearance. You may have to remove the door to plane any excess wood from the bottom; plane from the hinge and latch side of the door toward the middle.

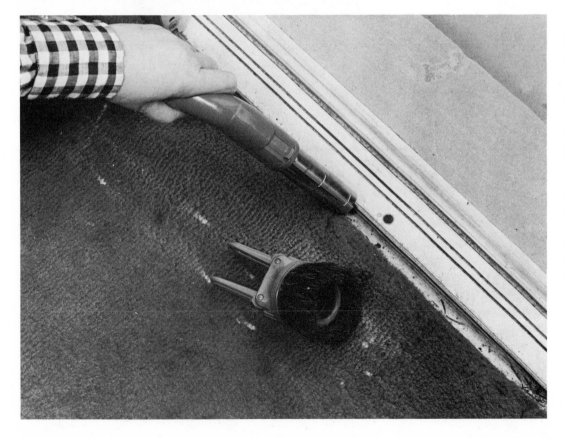

Patio door tracks should be vacuumed at least twice annually. Dirt and debris in the tracks can make the door hard to open and close, besides throwing it slightly out of alignment and causing air leaks. Also, large French doors leading to a patio or the outside of your home, if not glazed with thermal glass, should be weather stripped and/or covered with adequate storm windows during the winter months.

Malfunctioning rods which close storm doors can often be adjusted. Turn the screw at the end of the rod to tighten or loosen the tension. Also, make sure that the closing rod is properly lubricated with graphite powder. Graphite powder won't pick up dirt and dust as regular household oil does. If the closing rod is broken, replace it with a new one, which is simply screwed to the door and the doorframe. A new closer will cost about $4.

Tiny cracks between window stops (narrow strip to hold the casement in a window frame) and window frames can waste energy. If the cracks are fairly small, you may be able to tap the stop more closely against the window frame with a hammer and a piece of scrap wood, which acts as a buffer. Swing the hammer gently to avoid splitting the wooden stop.

If the crack between the window stop and the window frame is wide, you should reposition the stop. Pry off the stop with a thick bladed putty knife or a thin chisel. Remove the nails from the stop. Then, position the stop against the window; use a thin piece of cardboard between the stop and the window frame as a spacer. Renail the stop to the window frame with 6-penny (6d) finishing nails. Countersink the nailheads with a nail punch, and fill the holes with wood putty; then refinish the stop.

Misaligned doors, both exterior doors and interior passage doors between heated and unheated rooms, may cause a heat loss or gain. Loose door hinges may be the problem. If so, remove the hinge pins from the door, as shown. Use a piece of scrap wood to drive out stubborn pins; the wood will protect the metal.

Remove any screws from loose hinges, then fill the holes with kitchen matchsticks that have been dipped in glue. Break off each matchstick flush with the hinge and replace the screws, or you may replace the loose screws with longer screws. Also, you may fill the holes with steel wool and replace the screws.

If the door has a slight crack along the latch side, you may be able to shim out (level up to a desired height) the hinges far enough to close the crack and realign the door in its frame. Using light cardboard for the shim (filler), trace the outline of the hinge onto the cardboard, as shown. Then replace the hinges with the shim in back of each hinge leaf.

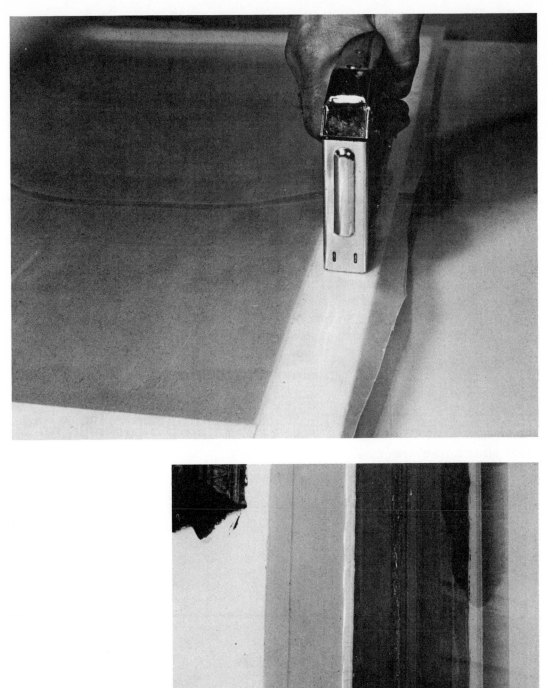

Screens may be converted into storm windows, if your budget will not permit permanent storm windows. Cover the screens with 2-mil polyethylene film and staple the film into position over the screening. Space the staples about 4 inches apart, and make sure the film is not puckered or gapped. Polyethylene film is also excellent for emergency repairs; for example, it may be used to seal the broken portion of a window. And, if shingles are blown from your roof, polyethylene film can be used to seal the roof until repairs can be made.

Permanent storm windows should be sealed with caulking compound. After you wash the inside of the storm window and the front side of the window that faces the storm window, caulk the joint between the window casing and the window frame. The storm window may be removed by first removing the bead of caulking. Storm windows that are used year-round prevent much heat loss during the winter and heat gain during the summer months.

Corner joints of storm windows often split open, causing heat loss or gain. Sometimes you can nail and glue the joints back together. If not, buy metal corner or joint braces to repair the window (or screen). The joint should be tightly pulled together; then nail the corner brace into place, as shown.

Seal your home's roof against energy loss

Roofing compound is available in caulking cartridges, or you can buy it in knife grade for sealing leaks on the roof. We recommend the cartridge tube in combination with a putty knife, which should be used to properly distribute the roofing compound. Look for air leaks around the chimney, soil stack vent, skylights, and ventilators. Apply plenty of roofing compound to the breaks.

Inspect roof valleys and apply asphalt roofing compound to any part of the metal that appears to be rusty or damaged. Also, inspect the chimney; if the mortar joints in the chimney are crumbling, clean them out and tuck-point them. (See *Stop Feeding the Energy Hogs* for tuck-pointing.) Also, caulk any exposed joints where the roofing meets a wooden structural member. The best time to make roofing repairs is in the spring or fall, when the sun doesn't soften asphalt shingles. If your roof has a steep slant, let a professional check it.

Secure loose asphalt shingles with a daub of roofing compound. If you have a wooden shingle roof on your house, check it for split shingles; these shingles may also be caulked with asphalt roofing compound. If you feel that you have a leak in the roof, fit a piece of aluminum sheet under the shingles that may be leaking; then, seal the edges of the aluminum with asphalt roofing compound. Also, look for exposed nailheads in the roofing; cover them with a daub of asphalt roofing compound.

Getting More Efficiency from Mechanical Equipment

Leaky faucets, dirty furnaces, overheating water heaters, and uninsulated heating and cooling ducts waste energy, which costs money.

The job of working with furnaces and air conditioning units should usually be left to a professional. However, there are several minor repairs that you can make which will save the cost of a service call. We explain how to make these repairs in this chapter.

Servicing a furnace or an air conditioner calls for a few basic tools: a screwdriver, a wrench, a hammer, and pliers. A malfunctioning furnace can be a great fuel waster. It should be cleaned annually by you or by a professional. For example, as carbon deposits itself on an oil furnace's heating tubes, these deposits act as a covering of insulation. Then the heat will go up the chimney. The serviceman should also analyze the carbon dioxide content of the gas in the flue (enclosed passageway). If the carbon dioxide is high, the combustion is satisfactory. If you hear rattles in the furnace, the fan, pump, or boiler may be defective and need servicing. And, if the chimney is smoking, the burner elements on the furnace may need to be adjusted.

Also, duct work from the furnace should usually be insulated to efficiently provide more heat.

Air conditioners need clean filters to properly function. If you have a central air conditioning system, it should be levelly mounted and the connections should be tight.

Annually inspect your water heater and keep it set at 140° to conserve energy.

How to clean a gas furnace

Turn off the furnace before you attempt to clean it. A turn-off switch is usually located in a junction box on the furnace housing, as shown. If you are not certain that the power is off after turning the switch, pull the plug at the main fuse box. If the furnace is a complex unit, call in a serviceman to do the cleaning job.

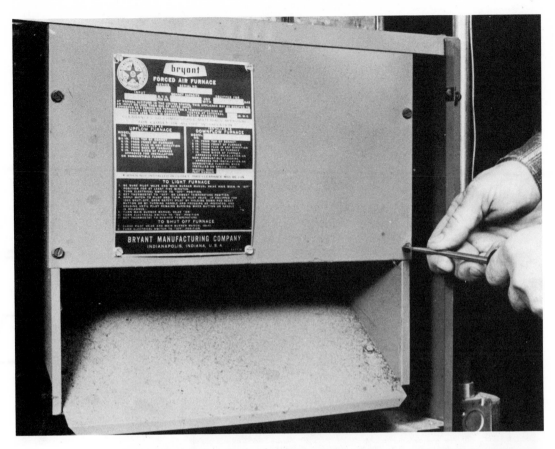

Remove the housing or sheet metal shell that covers the flue baffles (plates for deflecting gases or fluids). You will need a screwdriver or a nut driver for the job. Always work from the top down when cleaning a furnace, since the debris from each job falls downward. And keep the screws and bolts together as a unit so that reassembly will be easier.

A metal retaining strip holds the baffles in place. The strip is easily removed by backing out the screws that hold it in place. These screws generally have hexagonal screwheads, and you may need both a screwdriver and a nut driver to remove them. Avoid stripping the screwheads by using the correct screwdriver blade.

Mechanical Equipment   45

Remove the baffles, after the retaining strip is off, by sliding them out of the furnace; the baffles will easily slide out of the housing. Baffles usually have a gritty metalliclike substance in them. Dump out the debris, then wipe the baffles clean with an old cloth.

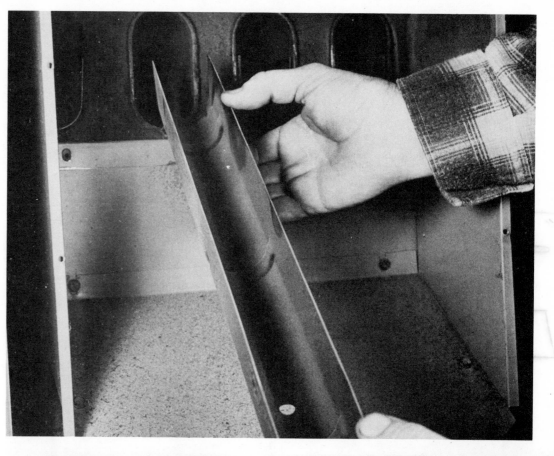

Vacuum the baffle housing and spend plenty of time using the vacuum so that the housing is thoroughly clean. A tubelike fitting is the best attachment to use on the vacuum. However, you may use a brush attachment if the housing is large enough to accept the brush. If you don't have a tube or brush attachment, use the metal end on the hose.

The burner section of the furnace is usually located under the baffles, and it is covered by a sheet metal housing. Remove the housing by backing out the screws that hold it in position. Keep the screws and parts together.

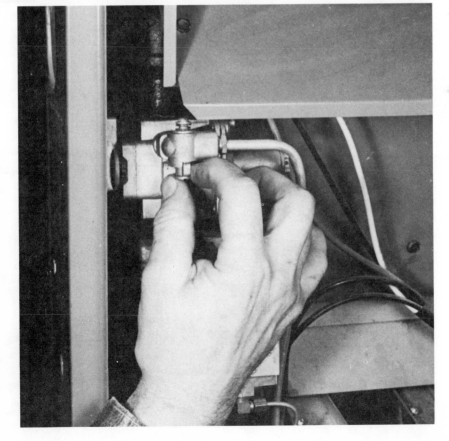

Burners should easily lift out of the furnace. If tubing is in the way, turn off the pilot light by rotating a small valve, as shown. The valve is marked. Directions for relighting the pilot light are usually printed on the furnace housing.

The end burner near the pilot light may be blocked by small tubing which is part of the thermal coupling. After the pilot light has been turned off, you can remove the coupling by unscrewing the coupling nut with a small wrench. Carefully move the tubing over so that you can remove the burner behind it.

A metal retaining strip may restrict you from removing the burners. This strip is similar to the baffle strip previously described, and it is actually a heat shield. To remove the strip, back out a set of screws along the top of it with a screwdriver or a nut driver.

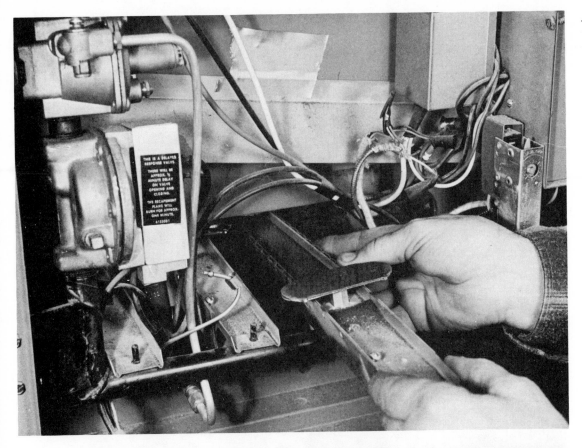

A small metal pin holds the burners in alignment. Release the pin to remove the burners, which slide out of the furnace, as shown. The burners are generally U-shaped, like baffles, and debris accumulates in the bottom portion of each burner. Dump out the debris and clean the burners with a cloth.

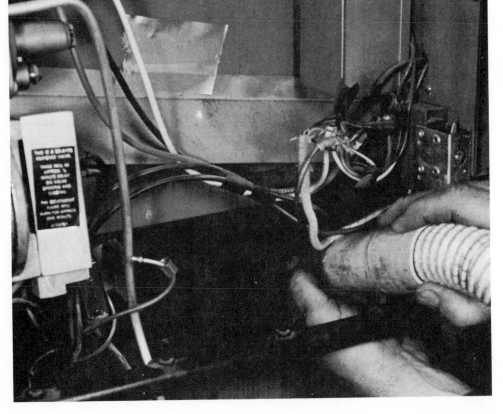

Vacuum the burner housings as you did the baffles. Then replace the burners and lock them into position with the tiny metal pins. Also, replace the heat shield strip and reconnect the thermal coupling pipe (disconnected earlier).

Some motor and blower housings on furnaces are sealed. Call a professional to open them for maintenance. Vacuum around these mechanical components to prevent dust from accumulating. If the motor is visible and has oil holes, give it several drops of No. 10 oil (or the manufacturer's recommended oil weight) twice annually. Also, inspect the V-belts that drive the blower; if the belts are frayed, replace them. Motor and blower pulleys should be tight on the drive shafts. If not, tighten them with an Allen (hexagonal) wrench or a regular screwdriver.

Change the filters on your furnace at least twice annually. If the heating season is a long one in your area, you may have to change the filters 3 or 4 times yearly. Central air conditioners often use the same filtering system as the furnace. Change the filter before the cooling season starts, and inspect it for dirt at least once during the season. The filters are inexpensive (about $1.25 each), and they are easy to change. You remove a metal plate near the blower unit to expose the filters. The airflow direction is marked on the filters.

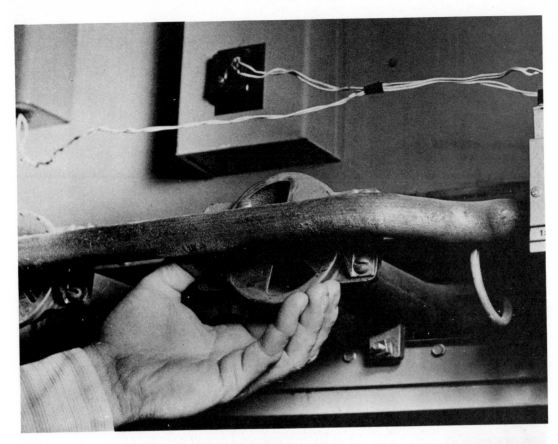

Some gas furnaces have air shutters that you regulate to conserve energy. If the flame is blue with a small yellow tip on the end, the furnace is functioning properly. If the yellow tip isn't present, the burners need more air. And, if the burner flame is too yellow, the system is getting too much air. You may be able to correct these problems by simply turning the air shutter.

Furnaces need air to burn properly. Make sure any doors that close off the furnace room are louvered to provide adequate air to the furnace. Shown is a combination of 3 raised panel and louvered doors which were used to supply needed air to the furnace. If the furnace room is a tightly closed area, doors with aluminum grill insets will provide enough air.

A furnace humidifier, properly set, can make rooms feel warmer without raising the energy output. For example, if the humidity is too low (below 40%) in your home, your body quickly loses moisture, and thus you feel cold. Low humidity can also dry out furnishings. Conversely, if the humidity is too high (above 60%) you will feel extremely warm.

Balance heating and cooling ducts. These ducts have baffles in them that control the output of hot or cold air in a warm air system. Simply turn the damper and check the heating or cooling flow. You may have to turn the damper several times to get the proper flow or balance of air.

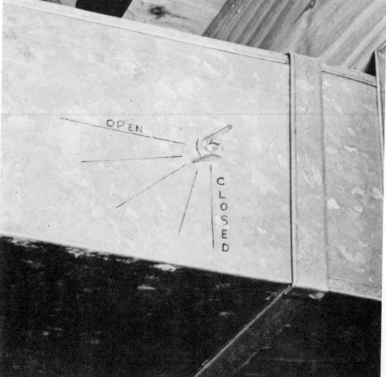

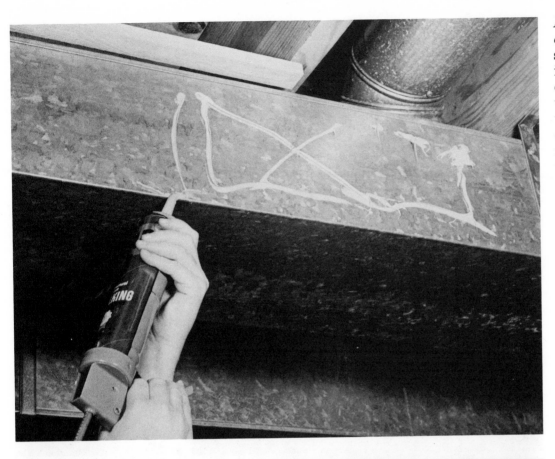

Insulate heating and cooling ducts with styrofoam or fiber glass insulation. Much energy can be lost when warm or cool air passes through noninsulated ducts in basement rooms or crawl spaces that are not heated or cooled. In an average house (about 1500 to 1800 square feet), a fuel savings of about $90 is possible with duct insulation. Insulation may be glued to the ducts or wrapped and tied. Spread the adhesive over the duct, as shown.

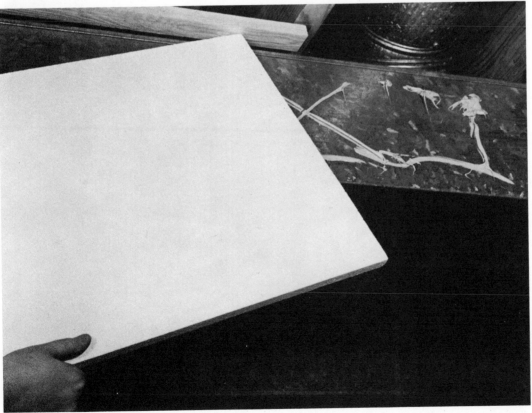

Insulation is pressed into the adhesive, then trimmed with a razor knife. Be sure all joints between the insulation are tight to prevent heat or cooling loss. Fiber glass insulation may be held to the ducts with adhesive and/or strapping tape. If the insulation has a vapor barrier, the barrier should face the room.

Do not insulate ducts in basement rooms that you frequently use. The heat or cooling loss through these ducts helps to heat or cool these rooms, and therefore saves money. If you are installing new heating and cooling equipment, buy the proper size for the space. Furnaces or air conditioning units are more efficient when they run at capacity or near capacity. Oversized equipment is expensive to buy and to operate.

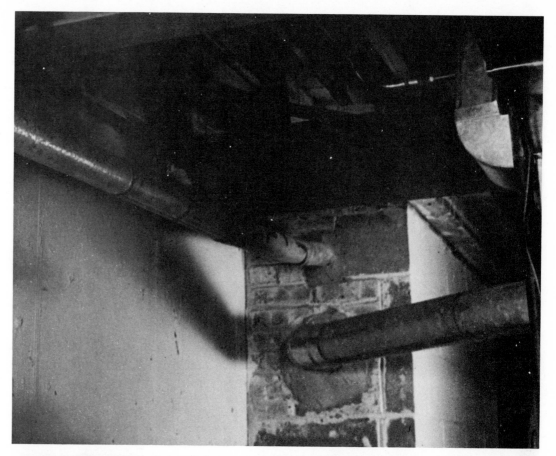

Check gas lines for tiny leaks. The leaks may be so small you can't detect them with your nose, yet, besides being dangerous, they can cause an energy loss. Mix a solution of water and detergent and apply this mixture with a brush to gas line joints. If you find a leak, try tightening the joint with a pipe wrench. If you are not successful, call in a serviceman immediately.

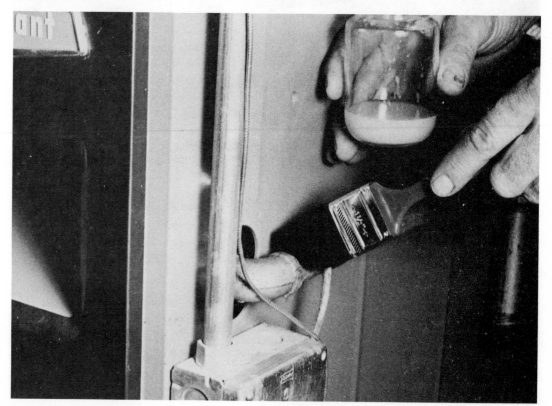

Fireplaces and the energy shortage

Prefabricated fireplaces that burn wood—especially those that have an electric blower to distribute the heat throughout the room—can help save on heating bills. Fireplaces operate best when your main thermostat for heat is located in another part of the house so that the thermostat setting remains constant. If the thermostat is located in the same room, you should turn it up. This setting will help stabilize the temperature in the rest of the house.

Always close the damper when the fireplace is not in use. The chimney can dispel more than 20% of the air heated by the furnace each hour the damper is open.

Gas-fired fireplaces or those that run on electricity may not be as aesthetic as their wood-burning counterparts, but they are more efficient in heating rooms and in supplementing heat provided by your furnace. This electric model has a thermostat to control the heat output in the room. These fireplaces are ideal for heating a special room such as a study, basement recreation room, family room, or a vacation cottage.

Buying and maintaining air conditioners

Although it would seem wise to buy an air conditioning unit that is overpowered for the space, the opposite is true. An overpowered window (or central) air conditioning unit wastes electricity and doesn't actually control the humidity within your home.

Air conditioning units are rated by BTUs. It takes about 18 BTUs an hour to cool 1 square foot of space. If you have 1000 square feet of space to cool, the unit should have an output of 18,000 BTUs. Personnel in the store where you buy your air conditioning unit will figure the exact amount of cooling power necessary for your home.

A central air conditioning unit costs about 20% less to operate than window units with the same cooling capacity; of course, the initial investment is somewhat greater.

Saving air conditioning energy

If you have window air conditioning units:

1. Level the unit on its brackets, especially if it has been stored all winter. Do not start the unit for 2 full days. Leveling permits the oil in the system to flow into the compressor component.

2. Clean the exposed surfaces.

3. Paint any sheet metal or exposed parts that have rusted; clean off the rust with a wire brush and steel wool. Then spot prime the area with metal primer. Coat the entire surface with a high quality metal paint to complete the job.

If you have a central air conditioning unit:

1. Reset the dampers in your home, if there are separate ducts for air conditioning.

2. Replace filters.

3. Check the auxiliary drain pan under the unit, if the air conditioner has one, to be sure the pan is clean and the drain works.

4. Start the air conditioner on a warm day and switch the thermostat from heating to cooling. The unit should operate smoothly. If not, call in a serviceman.

Basic air conditioning maintenance tips

Level the air conditioner. If the unit is not level, the oil in the compressor is not flowing properly. If the air conditioner sits on brackets, you may be able to adjust these to level the unit. If the air conditioner sits on a concrete pad, you will have to level the pad. Do this by digging dirt from underneath the pad; then pry it up with a pry bar, and force earth under the pad with a shovel. Or, level the unit on the pad with wooden shims.

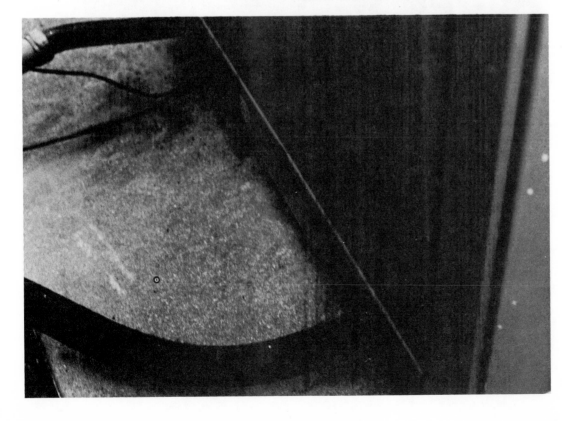

Carefully check hose connections. The connections should fit tightly to the outside part of the air conditioning unit and to the furnace inside your home. If the hoses are loose, use an auto hose clamp to tighten them. If the connection cannot be tightened, or if the hoses are damaged, call in a serviceman.

Replace or clean dirty filters in window air conditioners. Remove a panel on the front of the unit to reach the filters. Some filters may be washed in the kitchen sink, then lightly oiled; other filters have to be replaced. This information about type of filter is usually found in the owner's manual.

Right:
Vacuum coils in both central and window air conditioning units. If you can reach the motors, lubricate them at designated spots. Also, make sure that all vents are clean; they should not be obstructed by debris or blocked by overhanging bushes and trees.

Far right:
Roof ventilators that are powered by wind or electricity may allow you to save up to ⅓ on your cooling bill. Ventilators exhaust hot air from the attic when the temperature rises (up to 150°). Otherwise, the air radiates down to your living area and puts an extra load on your cooling equipment. Some ventilators have an automatic thermostat. To operate, set the thermostat; the ventilator will automatically shut off when the temperature drops 15°.

Ten ways to conserve air conditioning energy

There are several little tricks you can use during the summer months to help save air conditioning costs and energy. Here are 10 of them:

1. Cool air drops. When you are using a window unit, make sure that floor, sidewall, and low-return registers and grills are closed.

2. Turn off window air conditioners in rooms that are not occupied. If the room will periodically be occupied during the day, set the air conditioner at a temperature higher than the temperature setting in a room which is constantly occupied.

3. Shade window air conditioners from the sun with awnings.

4. If possible, place window air conditioners on the north side of the house.

5. If temperatures are low at night in your area, use an attic fan or an exhaust fan instead of air conditioning. Fans pull out hot daytime air and pull in fresh, cool nighttime air.

6. Turn off the air conditioning while you're on vacation.

7. Keep the thermostat set at 78°.

8. Leave storm windows and doors on in the summer months. Keep draperies closed—especially on windows that face the sun.

9. Weather strip all air leaks.

10. Check for leaks in ductwork. Leaks cause loss of cool air and heat.

How thermostats save energy

Keep heating thermostats constant. The best daytime setting is 68°. At night, turn the thermostat to about 63°. Do not set the thermostat at extreme high or low levels; moving the settings up and down actually costs money. If you are going on vacation or leave the house for a few days, set the thermostat at 55°. Every degree over 70° adds 3% to your heating charges. If you need heat in a hurry, move the thermostat to 72°; you will gain heat as quickly as you would by setting the thermostat at 80°. The higher setting will only overheat the house. However, if you have a 2-stage warm air system, you can heat a specific area faster with a high setting.

A *dirty thermostat* may malfunction and thus make the rooms in your home too hot or too cold. Inspect the working parts of the thermostat at least once a year. If the parts are dirty, clean them with a soft brush; do not oil the thermostat. Room thermostats should be located where the air circulates freely and away from fireplaces or room air conditioners, so that your original setting will remain constant. If the thermostat in your home is located next to hot-water pipes, in direct sunlight, near exterior doors, or next to heating ducts, you should consider moving it.

Saving hot-water heater energy

The cost of heating water for a family of four is about $140 annually. The thermostat on the hot-water heater should be set at 140° (normal). If you don't own a washing machine or a dishwasher, you can turn the thermostat down to about 110°. This is adequate for bathroom, kitchen, and laundry needs. It is estimated that hot water costs about $5 per month for every 10° setting over 120°. If your hot-water tank is leaking, replace it immediately; a new heater will cost from $100 to $150.

Drain a new hot-water heater every other month. Draining removes sediment, which can lower heating efficiency, from the bottom of the water tank. However, if your hot-water heater is an old one, do not drain it. Draining an old heater may cause sudden leaking problems. To drain a new hot-water heater, open the valve which is located near the bottom of the heater, as shown. Catch 1 or 2 quarts of water in a pail, then close the valve. Or, you may hook a garden hose to the valve and drain the water into a sink or floor drain. Let the water drain until it appears clean.

Insulate hot-water pipes to conserve fuel

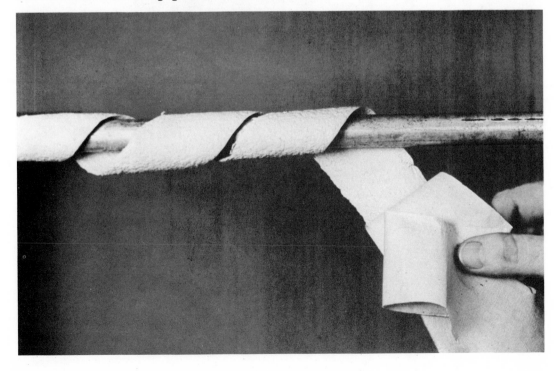

Transporting hot water from the water heater to a distant faucet can add to the cost of heating the water. You can solve this problem by insulating hot-water pipes, especially those with long runs to the faucets. This doughlike insulation is fairly inexpensive and easy to install. Wrap the insulation loosely around the pipes, then go back and push it tightly together. The material is soft (like modeling clay) and easy to form.

Insulation wraps easily around pipe joints. Cover the joints after the pipe has been covered with the material. The same material may be used for cold-water pipes that tend to drip with condensation during the summer months.

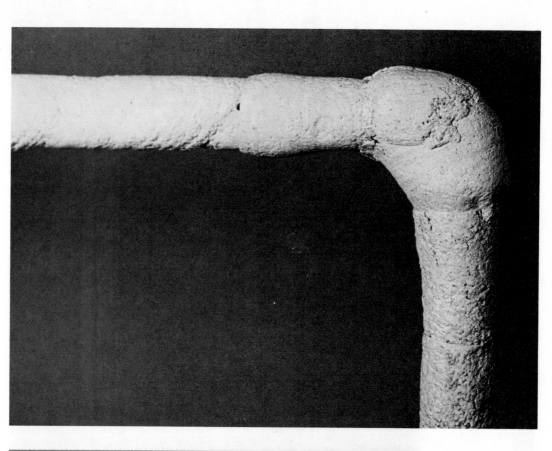

Fiber glass insulation with a special plastic wrapping may be used to seal hot- and cold-water pipes. First, coil the fiber glass insulation around the pipe, tack it down with a piece of masking or electrician's tape, and then seal the surface with the plastic vapor barrier. Special care must be taken to properly cover pipe joints. You'll probably have to cut the insulation slightly at the joints to make it fit smoothly.

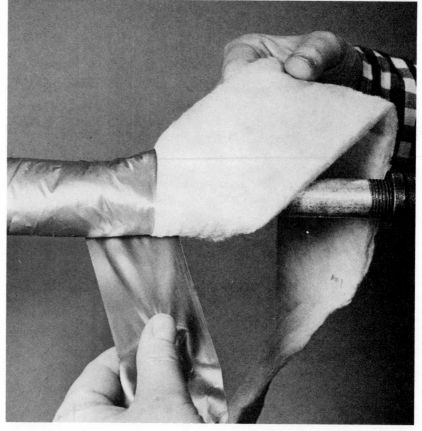

Leaky pipes can be expensive

Pinhole leaks in pipes not only rob you of energy and run up your bills, but they are also messy. In an emergency, you may prevent leakage by wrapping the pipe with plastic electrician's tape. It is only an emergency measure; the pipe should be replaced as soon as possible. A small leak will grow larger as water rushes through the pipe.

Special pipe clamps utilize a rubberlike gasket to stop water leaks in pipes. The clamps are screwed into position over a leak, as shown; they are a temporary, emergency measure. If the pipe is leaking, clamp it; then replace the pipe as soon as possible. For pinhole leaks in plastic and in copper pipe and tubing, try using electrician's tape around the leaks to stop the flow of water.

A temporary clamp for water leaks in pipes combines a C-clamp with a piece of rubber inner tubing or radiator hose. You simply wedge the rubber gasket between the jaws of the clamp; then turn the screw until the clamp is tight and the water flow has stopped. Hold the bottom of the clamp to the pipe as you turn the screw; it will keep the clamp from slipping off the pipe's round surface.

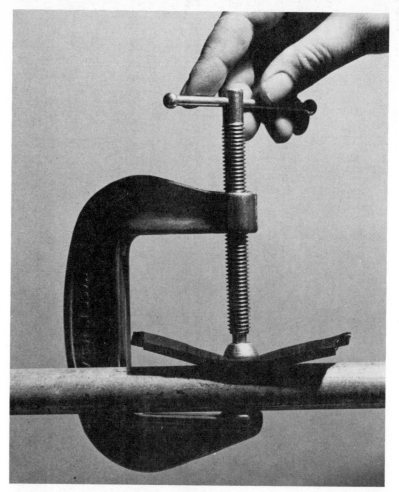

How to replace a leaky pipe

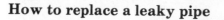

Cut the leaking pipe in half with a hacksaw after you turn off the water at the main valve. The main valve is usually located near the water meter on the inside of your home or near the hot-water heater. Before you start sawing the pipe, check the faucets to make sure the water is off; open both hot and cold water faucets in the bathrooms and kitchen.

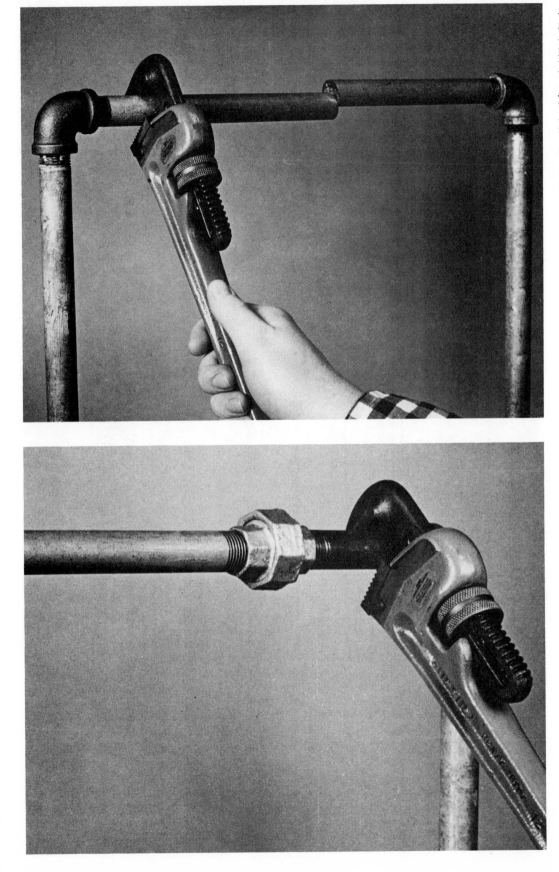

Remove the cut portions of the pipe with a pipe wrench. You may need a second pipe wrench to hold the joint or coupling tightly while you unscrew the pipe from the fitting. Use the pipe wrench with care to avoid damaging the joint fitting.

To replace the damaged pipe, you will need 2 sections of new pipe and a union fitting. The 2 pieces must be long enough to match the run; each piece will have an extra ½ inch of threads that will fit into the joint and the union. Assemble the pipe in sections as you replace it; don't preassemble the run. Wipe pipe joint compound on the male threads of the pipe to help prevent leaks at the joints. The pipe union fitting lets you assemble the run as a unit since the threads on the pipe turn one way on one end and in the opposite direction on the other end.

Leaky copper tubing may be replaced in the same way as galvanized steel pipe, as shown. First, turn off the water at the main valve. Then cut the bad pipe in half with a hacksaw or tubing cutter. Use a propane torch at the joints; the heat melts the soldered joint fittings so that you can remove the pipe. Cut a new length of copper pipe to replace the damaged pipe; make it long enough to properly fit into the fittings by allowing an extra ½ inch on each end. Test the tubing in the fittings; each end should fit tightly against the shoulder inside the fitting.

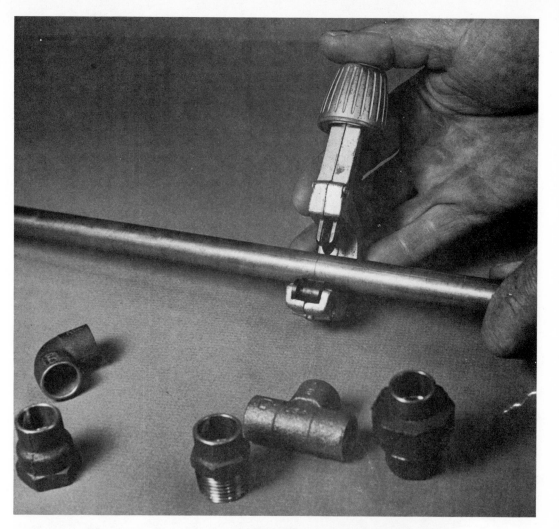

With a metal file, clean the burrs left by the hacksaw or tubing cutter from the tubing. Then shine the tubing with a piece of steel wool. The ends of the tubing must also be shiny and clean where they are inserted into a fitting. Daub the end of the tubing with soldering flux. Then assemble the entire run of pipe; make sure that all joints are square and solid.

Heat the joint where the 2 pieces of tubing meet with a propane torch. Then apply the wire solder to the joint between the tubing and the fitting. The heat will flow the solder into the joint. Do not heat the tubing, just the connection. The hottest part of the flame is the tip end. Fill the joint with solder and check it. The joint must be full or it may leak water. Also, don't do any soldering with water in the tubing; it will dissipate the heat.

Replacing plastic pipe

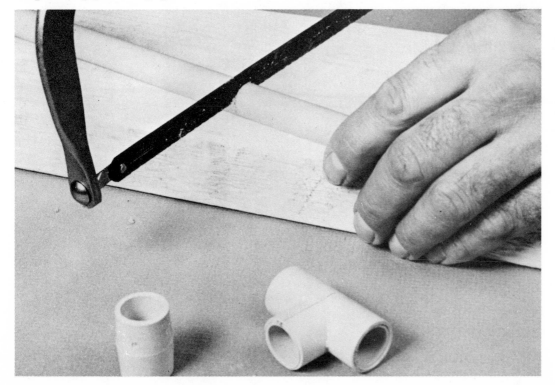

Damaged plastic pipe is easy to replace since it is easy to cut and to reassemble. First, turn off the water. Then cut out the damaged portion of plastic pipe with a hacksaw. Cut a new section to fit the old section. You'll have to allow about 1 inch more material on each end for the couplings.

Remove any burrs from the inside of the new plastic pipe with a sharp pocket knife. First, assemble the new run without cement (dry) by fitting the couplings tightly on the new and old pipe. Then cement the run together with plastic pipe cement. Once you have applied the cement, you can't remove the couplings or joints; thus, it is important to prefit the job.

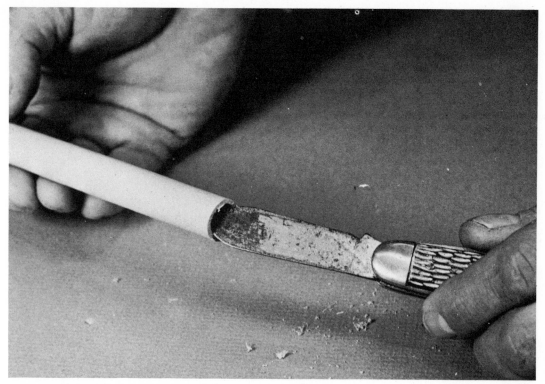

Leaky faucets

One drop of water every second from one leaky faucet wastes 700 gallons of water annually. If hot water is dripping, you also lose 5½ gallons of oil, or 700 cubic feet of gas, or 175 kilowatt hours of electricity (used to heat the water). Leaky faucets are easy to repair. First remove the cap covering the stem of the faucet; it is usually held by a single screw, as shown. Make sure the tip of the screwdriver fits the screw slot. Otherwise, the screwdriver may slip out of the slot and damage the chrome or plastic handle and cap. But before you start, turn off the water at the main entry.

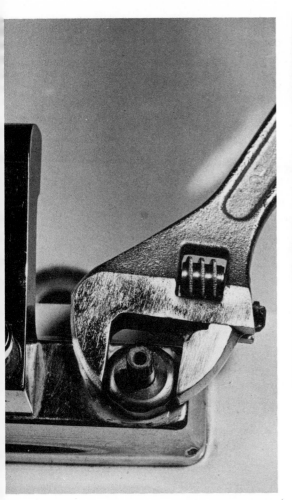

Far left:
Remove the stem from the faucet housing. Use an adjustable wrench or smooth-jawed pliers to avoid damaging the stem. Pull against the fixed jaw of the wrench. If the stem is difficult to remove, don't force it. Instead, squirt a couple of drops of penetrating oil around the stem cap. The oil will loosen the corrosion that is probably holding the stem.

Left:
The stem twists out with finger pressure. If the stem is unscrewed and suction is holding it in position, screw the handle of the faucet back on the stem assembly and use the handle to lift out the stem. Then remove the handle.

The stem may be corroded. If so, clean off the corrosion with fine steel wool. Use a soft cloth to wipe the stem with mineral spirits. This will remove any fine strands of steel wool that are left on the stem.

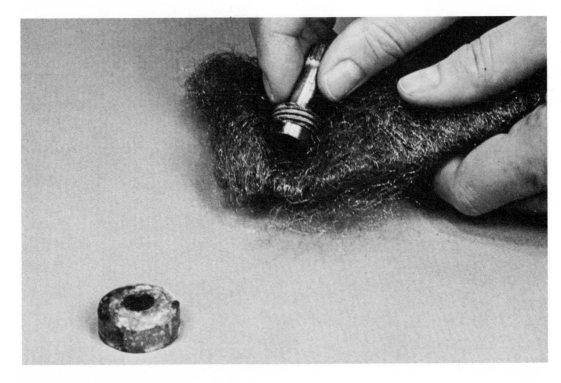

The faucet washer is located on the bottom of the stem assembly; it is held in place with a tiny roundhead brass screw. Back out this screw to remove the washer from its seat. Match the new washer to the washer seat and screw it into position. You can buy polybags of different sized washers at most hardware stores and home center outlets. The cost is only about $1 per bag. Some assortments even include new brass screws to hold the washers in place.

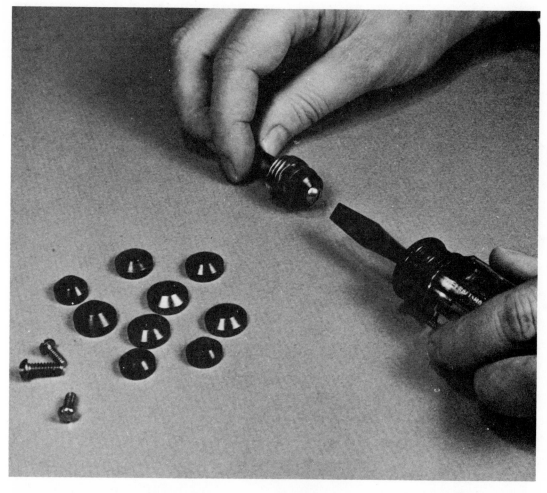

O-ring washers are found in some standard faucets. These washers usually don't have to be replaced. However, if the O-ring washer looks damaged, put on a new one. O-ring washers are most often included in flat washer assortments.

Cap packing may be a twinelike product that you wrap around the stem at the cap, or the packing may be similar to a washer. If the cap is leaking at the faucet, first try tightening it with a wrench. If the cap continues to leak, you will have to replace the packing.

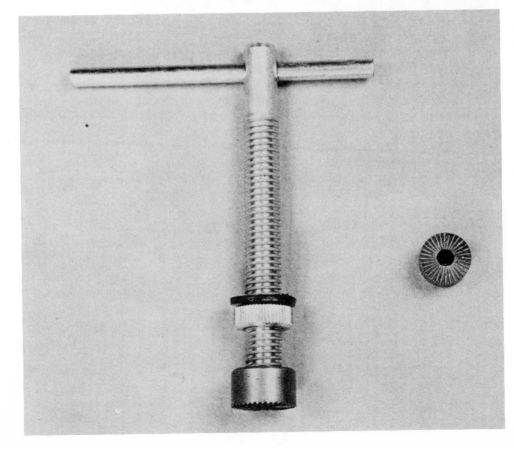

The faucet seat or valve seat may be damaged, which will cause the faucet to leak. You can repair it by grinding the seat with this special tool (about $4). However, if the faucet is an old one, you may want to consider replacing the entire faucet, which will cost from $5 to $10, depending on the type of faucet.

The grinding tool is inserted through the cap of the faucet. The cap is then screwed to the faucet. As you turn the grinding tool into the faucet, the tiny ridges on the bottom of the tool will smooth the seat inside the faucet.

Single handle faucets are usually dripless. However, once in a while an O-ring will become damaged and cause the faucet to leak around the handle. If you have a leak, remove the faucet handle which is usually held in place with a screw. You will have to remove a cover plate first; it snaps into position with tiny friction teeth. Then remove the spindle. This comes out when you lift a tiny ring at the top of the spindle housing.

Remove the spindle by pulling it straight out of the housing. This will expose the O-rings which slide off and on. If the bottom section of the spindle looks damaged, it is wise to replace the entire spindle. Take the old spindle to a plumbing outlet to match the new spindle with the old.

Improving Radiator Efficiency

If your home is equipped with radiators (a hot-water heating system), they need to be bled annually. It will be necessary to open a bleeder valve that is usually located on top of the radiator at one end. Unscrew the valve carefully. You may hear a hissing noise; then water will flow from the valve. Close the valve and move on to the next radiator.

If the valve is leaking, try to remove it; then soak the valve in a boiling mixture of baking soda and water. Let the valve boil for 30 minutes. Then replace it. If the valve still leaks, you will have to buy a new one.

A leaky radiator valve may be repaired by turning the collar of the valve with a wrench. If this doesn't work, unscrew the collar, and repack the valve with new packing or a washer.

Saving Automobile Energy

As we all know, the federal speed limit has been pushed back to 55 miles per hour to save fuel. How much gasoline does this really save? Statistics show that you will save about 25% of your fuel by slowing the car from 70 mph to 50 mph. A large part of this fuel savings is from reduced wind resistance. The faster you drive, the more wind resistance there is. Thus, it takes more gas to resist the wind which builds up in front of your car like snow builds up on the blade of a snowplow.

Energy-saving checklist

Driving more slowly isn't the only answer to saving fuel. Below, you'll find a checklist of proven fuel-saving ideas.

☐ Start your car smoothly. To suddenly hit the floorboard with the accelerator from a stationary position wastes much gasoline, besides being damaging to the car's power train and tires. A smooth start is a sign of a good driver.

☐ Drive your car at constant speed.

☐ Share your car with others whenever possible. Car pools take a little planning, but they save fuel and money.

☐ Use public transportation whenever possible. Or, if your destination isn't too far, walk. Walking is not only good for you but also saves gas. Driving a short distance in your car can decrease gasoline savings by 60%.

☐ Air conditioning is delightful on very hot days; however, it will utilize about 10% more fuel than is normally used. When days are not too hot, open the car windows.

☐ Make sure the wheels of your car are aligned and the tires are properly balanced. Wheels that are not aligned will contribute to wasting gas, and unbalanced tires will wear out faster.

☐ When you have several errands to run, plan the trip. Taking a back road may save gasoline. A heated auto engine will save as much as 70% more fuel than a cold engine.

☐ If you must travel in your business, rent a small economy car to get around. A small car uses less gas and costs less to rent.

☐ Don't warm up the engine in your car or let it idle. Even when the temperature dips low, you should only let the car warm up for about 30 seconds. Drive slowly for the first mile; this will compensate for the lack of warm up time.

☐ Don't overload the trunk of your car.

☐ Keep your foot off the brakes as you drive. Every time you hit the brake, you have to speed up again, which wastes gas.

☐ Drive in high gear; lower gears waste gasoline. If you have a stick shift, go through the gears quickly and shift to a lower gear only if the speed calls for it. Also, if your car has an automatic transmission, do not activate the passing gear unless absolutely necessary; it takes extra gasoline.

☐ Keep your car in a garage, if possible. Your car will be easier to start on cold days, and this easier start will save fuel.

☐ Your car's manifold heat control valve should be serviced about every 6 months. This valve allows the exhaust gas to heat the intake manifold of the car when the engine is cold. If the valve is stuck in an open position, the engine will heat slowly. If the valve is stuck in a closed position, the engine will be difficult to start.

☐ Automatic chokes that are improperly adjusted may cause loss of fuel. Have the automatic choke tested every 6 months.

☐ Check the fan and the air conditioning belts twice annually; a worn or slipped belt can cause problems.

☐ Install an antisurge cap on the gas tank to prevent spillage.

Engine tune-ups are critical to saving gasoline. Malfunctioning spark plugs will provide poor engine performance, and when they are not kept serviced, they must be replaced. Also, if the engine's timing is off, the engine will not fire properly and will waste fuel. We recommend that you have an engine tune-up every fall and spring.

Inspecting an air filter is an easy job. If the air filter is dirty, the car loses power and gas. The air filter should be changed about every 12,000 miles. If you live in an area that is sandy or dusty, check the air filter about every 3,000 miles. To get to the air filter, turn a wing nut on top of the plate that covers the filter.

Tire air pressure can be critical in saving fuel, and it will affect the wear-and-tear on the tires. Tires without enough air pressure can also be dangerous. Check the air pressure at least once a month; also, check the pressure when there is a dramatic temperature change. However, don't inflate the tires more than the manufacturer's recommended maximum tire pressure.

Your Lawnmower Can Waste Gas, too

When conserving energy, don't overlook your lawnmower which can waste a gallon or so of gasoline every time you cut the lawn. This may not seem like a lot of wasted energy, but multiply your lawnmower by the millions of units in the United States, and the figure becomes impressive. And there is a gasoline cost factor to consider.

Fortunately, making carburetor adjustments to your lawnmower is not difficult. These parts are involved: the power adjusting needle, an idling adjustment screw, the idle speed adjustment screw, the spark plug, and the air cleaner.

1. Change the park plug or have it cleaned at your local service station at the beginning of each grass-cutting season.

2. Close the power adjusting needle. The needle has a small knob, usually on the carburetor. Turn this needle so it is competely closed. Then open the needle one turn.

3. Close the idle adjusting needle. Turn it until the needle stops turning. Now, open the needle about a ¾ turn.

4. Start the lawnmower engine. Open the throttle slowly until the throttle is at full power. Now give the power adjusting needle about a ⅛ turn until the engine is running smoothly. Move the needle back and forth until the engine fires properly. You can hear and feel it.

5. Close the throttle lever, and adjust the idle adjusting needle until the engine is running smoothly.

Also make sure the air filter is kept clean. Your lawnmower may have a throw-away filter, or it may have the plastic washable type. If it is the latter, wash the filter at least three times during the grass-cutting season.

Stop Feeding the Energy Hogs

In this chapter, you will find numerous energy-saving tips and techniques. It is important to keep in perspective the amount of energy that various appliances in your home use. Dishwashers, freezers, ranges, and water heaters all use many kilowatt hours of electricity, but toasters, electric knives, and waffle irons use very little electricity. Remember also that broken windows, leaky foundation walls, and malfunctioning exhaust fans will drain energy. By becoming aware of the ways you may lose energy in your home, you may be able to take a few steps to prevent loss of energy.

Replacing broken windows

A broken window sash (glass) or broken storm windows and doors will cause energy to be quickly lost. Even a small section of cracked glass can reduce heating and cooling efficiency. To repair a broken window, first remove the broken glass. Wear gloves to protect your hands, and remove as much broken glass as possible.

Some windows (especially storm windows) have tiny wooden strips that help hold the glass in the window frame. Find the key strip of wood; it usually fits against the face of a side strip. Break the paint seal between the strip and the window frame with a sharp razor knife.

Pry the holding strips loose. A stiff-bladed putty knife or a wide flat chisel makes a good prying tool. Be careful not to split the holding strip. If you do split the strip, save the pieces; you may be able to patch them later. If you can't use the old strips, you can buy new ones at a building material store.

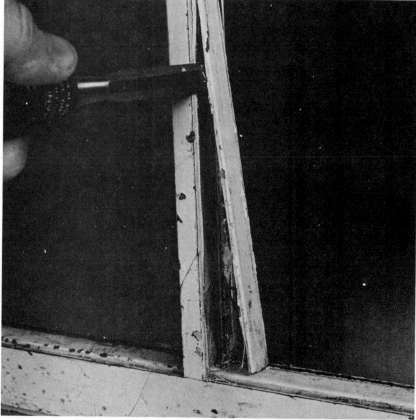

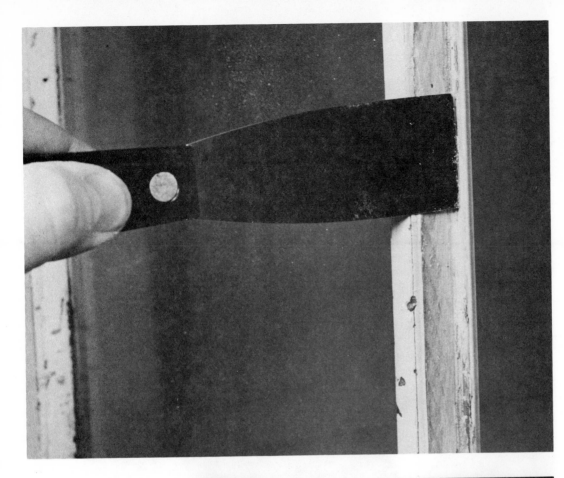

Remove all broken glass from the channels of the frames (mullions). The channels have to be clean and smooth to accept the new glass. If the window is glazed with glazing compound, remove all of the old glazing with a putty knife. Also, remove the metal glazier's points that held the old glass in position.

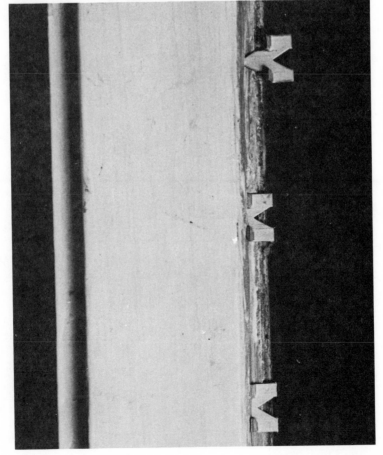

Install new glass in the frame. If glazing is used, secure the glass with glazier's points. The points are pressed into position—about 3 to 4 inches apart. If the glass is held in the frame with strips, tack them in, and attach the key strip last. We recommend tempered replacement glass which is stronger than regular glass. If tempered glass is broken, it will shatter into small pieces rather than large jagged ones. The glass for the window should be cut about 1/16 or 1/8 inch smaller than the opening to be filled.

Prime the glass and the wooden frame with paint for a good seal. Let the paint run about ¼ inch onto the glass, as shown. If strips are used to hold the glass in the window, seal both the window and the back of the strips with paint.

Wipe in glazing compound after the paint has dried. Ball the compound in your fingers and position it against the glass. Then use the putty knife to form a 45° angle between the glass and the edge of the frame. First, approximate the angle, and then fill it.

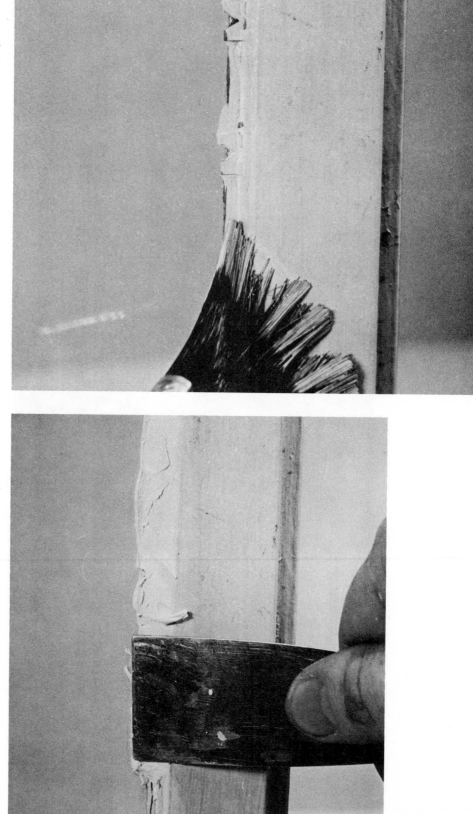

Smooth the glazing compound with the tip of the putty knife. Run the knife at a 45° angle along the glass; let one edge of the knife move along the glass and the flat part of the blade run along the frame. The angle helps to provide a smooth, consistent job. If the putty knife seems to pick up the glazing compound, scour the blade by jabbing it into the earth or polish the blade with steel wool.

Storm windows with metal frames usually have a rubber or plasticlike gasket that holds the window in the frame. First, remove all broken glass from the frame, and then pry the frame apart at the mitered corners. The corners may be held by a screw in the edge of the window frame. The trick is to apply the gasket to the edge of the glass. Then place the glass in the frame and push it into position. You may have to experiment several times to make the unit fit. Use a mild solution of soap on the gasket and frame to help the gasket slide easily into the frame.

Splines and screws hold some metal storm windows together. The gasket for the glass may be made of felt rather than rubber or plastic. The technique for installing the glass in the metal frame is similar to the one mentioned above. If the window is the thermal type with double glass (for example, a patio window), broken glass should be replaced by a professional since a special seal is required.

Storm windows and draperies can save heat/cooling

Storm windows can reduce the heat loss or gain up to 50%. Although costly, storm windows and doors should pay for themselves over a period of six years. Awnings, roof overhangs, attic and window fans also help lessen heat loss or gain. You may pull draperies to save energy. In the winter, open draperies on windows that face the sun to take advantage of solar heat. In the summer, close draperies that face the sun to block out heat.

Double-insulated window glass is available for some windows. Also, consider heat-absorbing or reflecting glass. This specially colored glass can reduce heat generated by direct sunlight by 40 to 70%. Metal-framed windows should be double glazed to reduce heat and cooling loss.

Foundation walls can be a source of energy loss

Cracks and crumbling mortar in masonry foundation walls let air in and out and sometimes let in unwanted water. Fill and tuckpoint these breaks with epoxy mortar mix which is found at building material stores. First, clean the cracks or breaks with a brick chisel to remove all loose mortar and other debris. If the crack is in a poured concrete foundation, cut an inverted V below the crack. The V shape helps hold the mortar in position.

Wet the break with water to clean and prepare it for mortar mix. Use plenty of water for deep penetration. These same techniques are used to patch chimney bricks and concrete blocks—as well as brick foundations, as shown.

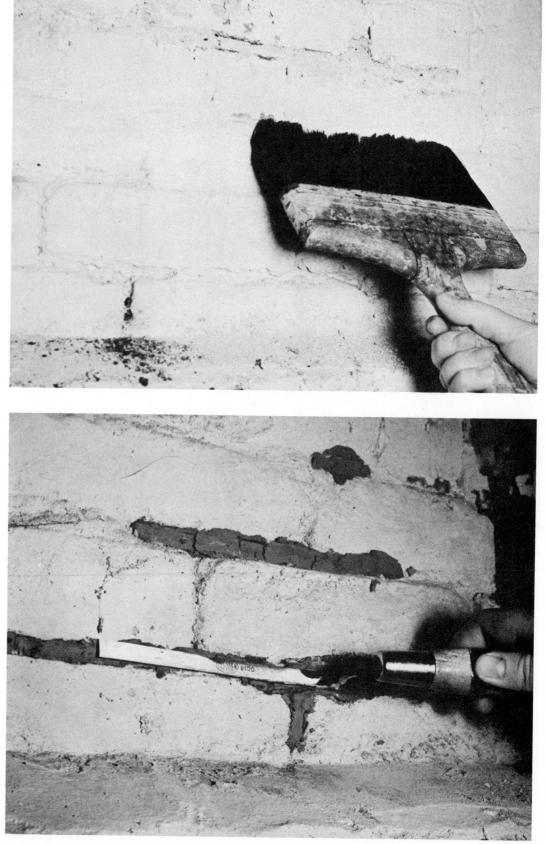

Press the mortar mix into the break. It is best to use a tuck-pointing trowel, although you may be able to substitute a putty knife. Tuck-pointing trowels cost about $2. When the break is completely full of mortar mix, smooth the joint slightly with the trowel.

Smooth the mortar mix with a joint strike (rounded piece of metal) after it has set for 15 minutes. A joint strike costs about 75¢. Run the strike firmly over the mortar joint; it helps push the mortar into the break. It also gives the joint a concave configuration, which helps drain water during rainstorms.

Getting the most out of your appliances

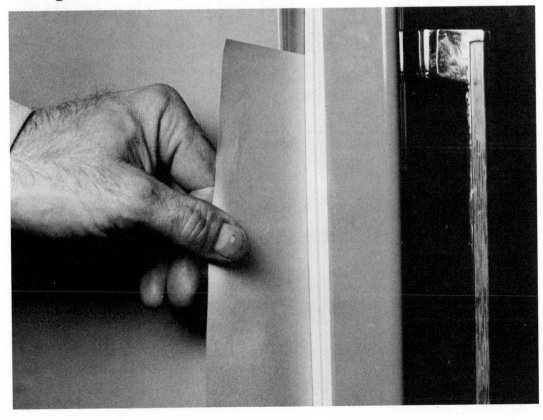

Leaky refrigerator seals contribute to wasting energy. Test for seal leaks by inserting a piece of paper between the seal and the doorframe of the unit. When you pull on the paper, it should be fairly difficult to remove. If the paper slides out easily, the seal around the door probably should be changed.

Tighten the refrigerator door seal, if possible, by adjusting the tiny screws that hold it in position. You may have to slightly loosen the screws. This will release the seal so that it fits more firmly against the door. It is a trial-and-error technique. Loosen each screw only slightly; then do the paper test.

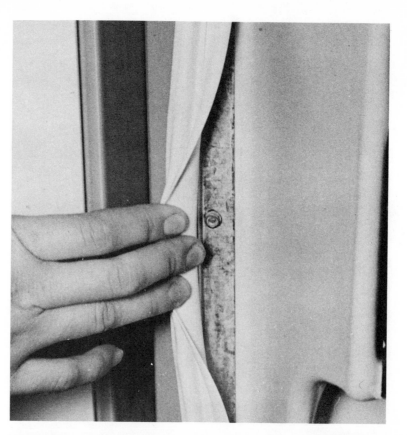

Keep the refrigerator coils clean by vacuuming them at least twice annually. Also, keep the cooling coils clean. More than ¼ inch of ice on the coils serves as an insulation barrier and will reduce cooling power. Check refrigerator latches and hinges. Loose latches and hinges may cause gaps in the door seal, but they can usually be tightened with a screwdriver.

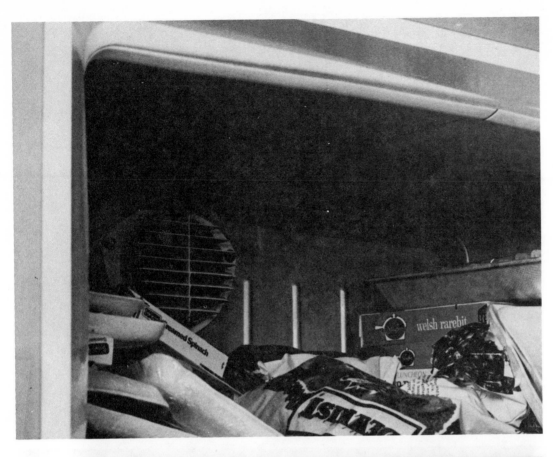

Locate refrigerators away from heating appliances such as ranges and ovens. Also, don't locate the refrigerator over a heating duct or against a window. Fans in the freezer section must not be blocked by frozen foods; they need to circulate air within the compartment. If blocked, the fan loses efficiency. If you are going to invest in a new refrigerator, consider a manual defrost model. The manual unit takes about two-thirds less electricity to operate.

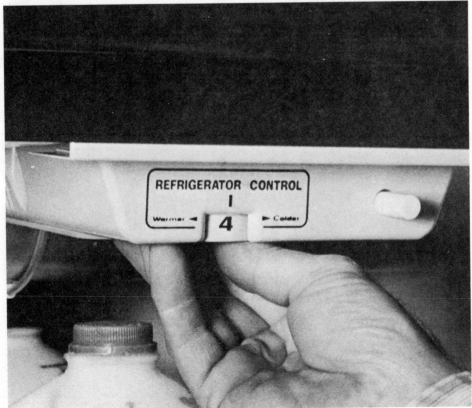

Keep refrigerator and freezer thermostats at normal levels. If the setting is too cold, you will waste electricity. Also, don't put hot dishes directly into the refrigerator; let the food cool first. Always fill the refrigerator to capacity, but don't overload it; a full refrigerator operates more economically.

Fit pans to burners. Putting a small pan over a large burner wastes heat. Also, use flat-bottomed pans with straight sides on surface burners, and cover them with lids. Cook with a small amount of water; it will heat quickly, which saves energy. Frozen vegetables can cook in 2 to 4 tablespoons of water; use about ½ cup of water for fresh vegetables.

Keep gas burners clean. If ports become clogged with food debris, use a needle or a piece of wire to clean them. Do not use wooden matchsticks; they may break off in the ports. If you own a temperature-controlled stove, use a fine piece of metal or wire to clean the diagonal slits in the tower pilot burners. Always wipe up spills and splatters as soon as possible.

See-through oven doors save energy because you don't have to continually open the door to check food. Microwave ovens utilize about 20% less energy than a regular oven. Self-cleaning ovens consume about the same amount of energy as regular ovens, if the units are properly insulated. Clean a self-cleaning oven only when the oven is hot from cooking. Try to use your oven broiler for cooking, since it doesn't need to be preheated.

You lose 20% of the heat in your oven each time the door is opened; don't peek unless it is absolutely necessary. Also, plan your cooking: if you have several dishes to cook which use about the same oven temperature, set the oven at a mean temperature for all the dishes and remove each dish as it is cooked. When cooking in glass and ceramic dishes, you may set your oven 25° lower; these dishes retain heat and save energy. Don't preheat the oven; most foods that require a full hour or more of cooking do not have to be placed in a warm oven. Never use your oven as a room heater.

Thaw frozen foods before cooking them. Use a food warmer, if you have one. The warmer costs less to operate than the oven or surface units. Also, be sure the burners and oven are turned off after the food has been prepared.

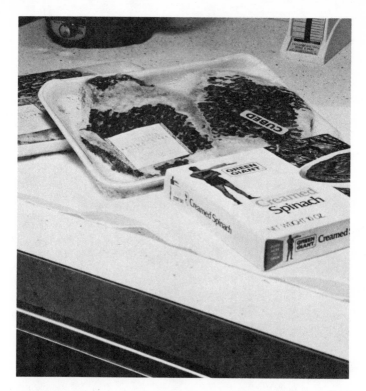

Dishwasher and washer/dryer tips

Always fully load your dishwasher. Don't wash partial loads; scrape and stack breakfast and luncheon dishes, and wash them with the dinner dishes. Also, load the dishwasher properly; use adequate detergent so that you don't have to rewash the dishes, and scrape off food debris to prevent it from clogging the pump. Inspect the drain weekly to make sure it is clean. Use cold water in garbage disposals. Cold water will consolidate the grease so that it may be flushed down the drain. Let the water run for several minutes after the motor has been turned off; it will help to clean the trap in the disposal.

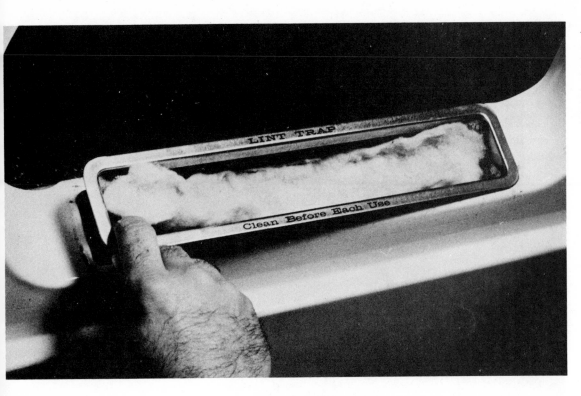

Keep clothes dryer temperatures low. Also, partly dry clothes to prepare them for ironing. If your unit doesn't have a damp-dry cycle, remove the clothes when they are only slightly damp. Use a warm setting for permanent press clothes; promptly remove them when they are dry. Make sure the lint filter is cleaned after each load of clothing (as shown). Also, if possible, locate the dryer in a warm part of the room.

Keep the water level low in your washing machine. It doesn't take much energy to operate the washer, but it does take considerable energy to heat the water. Use mini-wash cycles and wash in cold water whenever possible.

Use cold water in washers when you use cold water detergents. Permanent press fabrics may be washed in warm water; woolen fabrics may be washed in cold water. Irons take a lot of energy to heat. Start with synthetic fabrics on a low setting, and then iron silk and wool fabrics at a slightly higher setting. Move to high temperatures for cottons and linen. Starting the iron on a low temperature lets the iron gradually build up heat, which conserves energy.

Keeping grills and ducts clean

Exhaust fans over ranges and in bathrooms, as well as their filters, should be cleaned at least twice yearly. Smoke and odors will be quickly eliminated through clean grills.

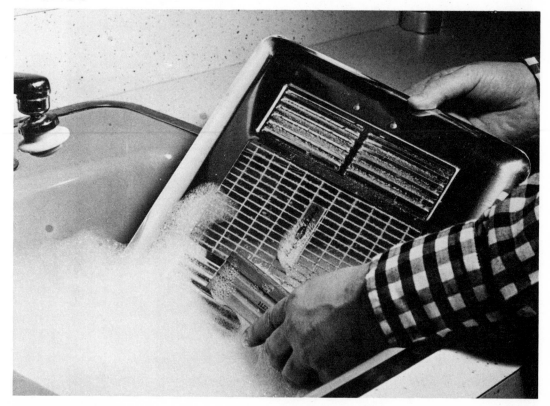

Vacuum heating and cooling ducts in warm air heating systems. Clogged ducts and registers make your furnace and air conditioner work harder to distribute warm or cool air. Also, make sure that your clothes dryer vent is free from lint and dirt. Disassemble it from the dryer once a year and vacuum the debris, or pull a cloth sack full of newspaper through the vent pipe.

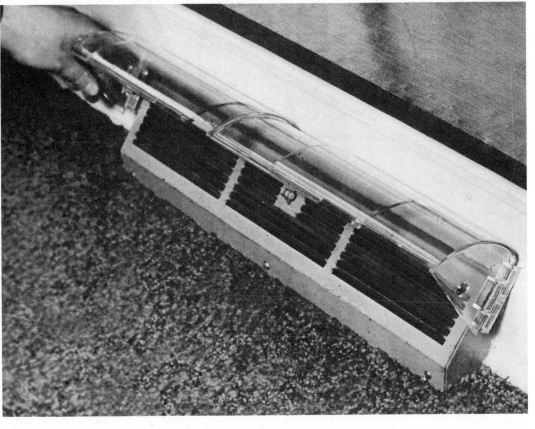

Register deflectors sometimes help to distribute warm air throughout rooms, which cuts costs. The deflectors may also be used to distribute cool air. Deflectors cost about $3 per unit. Do not cover registers and ducts with draperies or set furniture in front of these outlets.

Television sets that have no warm-up time use about one kilowatt hour every 24 hours. When you go on vacation or leave your house for the day, unplug the set. Also, turn off the set when no one is watching it. Timers and photoelectric cells will automatically turn off exterior lights and those in your home; the timer (shown) plugs into an outlet, and the cord to the electrical device is plugged into the timer.

All About Lighting

It costs about $30 per year to continually burn a 100-watt light bulb. If you consider the number of light bulbs in your home, even though they may not burn for 24 hours or be 100-watt bulbs, you can see how your electricity bill could mount. Try to use zoned lighting for special purposes such as reading, watching television, washing dishes, and doing laundry.

Here are some lighting facts:

• Fluorescent lighting saves electricity. A 40-watt fluorescent fixture (bulb) provides more light than a 100-watt incandescent light bulb. The fluorescent bulb also costs half as much to operate as the incandescent light, and the bulb lasts 10 times longer.

• Brightness of a light bulb is measured in lumens. A watt refers to the amount of electricity it takes to make a bulb work. Check the lumens for the size bulb you need for a specific area.

• Always turn off lights when you leave a room.

Index